HIERARCHICALLY

ORGANIZED SYSTEMS

IN THEORY & PRACTICE

By PAUL A. WEISS

WITH CONTRIBUTIONS BY:

H. K. BUECHNER, J. S. COLEMAN, J. W. FORRESTER
K. LORENZ, D. McNEILL, H. OZBEKHAN

Hierarchically
Organized Systems
in
Theory and Practice

Hierarchically Organized Systems in Theory and Practice

by
Paul A. Weiss

With contributions by:

H. K. BUECHNER, J. S. COLEMAN, J. W. FORRESTER
K. LORENZ, D. McNEILL, H. OZBEKHAN

HAFNER PUBLISHING COMPANY
New York
1971

Published by
HAFNER PUBLISHING COMPANY, INC.
866 Third Avenue
New York, N.Y. 10022

Library of Congress Catalog Card Number: 72-147275

Printed in U.S.A. by
NOBLE OFFSET PRINTERS, INC.
NEW YORK 3, N. Y.

Foreword

The first article of this book sets the main theme in focus. Entitled "The Basic Concept of Hierarchic Systems," it was originally written as the Introduction to a reprinted version of my textbook on "Principles of Development," of thirty years' earlier vintage. In the intervening period, a marked trend toward thinking in terms of "systems" concepts had emerged in science, as well as in many other areas of human activities and public concern (e.g., traffic, economics, environment, natural resources, community planning). This has made it appear desirable to give the student, and through him, to a wider sector of society, at least some inkling of the profound conceptual change that thus has been set in motion.

The present booklet is a sketchy answer to that need. Its scope is modest. It is confined (1) to demonstrating the logical cogency of a "systems" concept of the world, and indeed, the rational superiority of its flexibility over the rigidity of the conventional, scientifically outdated, notion that the Universe, including man, operates as a microprecise "cause-effect" mahcine; and (2), to indicating, by a very few examples, the wide bearing of the principle on age-old problems and on man's coping with ever new emerging ones.

A conceptual change is not like a change of style in clothes, which one can follow in total ignorance of the origin and manufacture of textiles. Concepts, being products of the mind, cannot be understood unless they are traced back to their roots in human cognition. This I have tried to do for the "systems" concept in the first part of the booklet. I hope my confidence in the didactive efficacy of a book is not misplaced. Let me just ask, therefore, right at the start just what it is that such a booklet could at all hope to accomplish in recasting into fresh and more adaptive molds the hardened habits of traditional thinking.

A book is a means of communication—communication of information, of rules, of thoughts. Its tools are the symbols of language—numbers, words, terms. Tools in continual use tend to become blunted and need resharpening if they are to remain useful. Obsolete tools must be refitted or be discarded. Scientific language, as the tool for the articulation of scientific knowledge, must be kept in step with the advance of knowledge. Yet, as refined knowledge keeps calling for refinements in the language to express it, the habitual inertia of established language, conversely, acts as a drag on the extrication of thought from ruts grooved by tradition. Instead of adapting our accustomed tools of expression to the widening scope of new insights into nature, we often, unwittingly, try to constrain nature, or rather our views of it, into the narrow box of our traditional ways of representing it. In other words, habits of language tend to force patterns of thought into rather rigid molds. In order to preclude this shackling of the progress of knowledge, one must keep a constant check on the intellectual and verbal tools in use for communicating knowledge truthfully, unequivocally, and intelligibly, to decide whether they are still adequate.

As an incentive and start for such a critical assessment, I shall briefly outline the conceptual tools and operations through which scientific knowledge is gathered, ordered, shaped and communicated. The intent is to bring these *intellectual* tools to a standard of precision and cleanliness comparable to that taken for granted in the use of our *technical* tools. Being necessarily brief and sketchy, the outline cannot hope to overcome all the internal residues of deeply ingrained habits of descriptive speech. Yet, if it helps to set the stage for the development of a frame of mind that will embrace new ways of viewing, thinking about, and dealing with, the real world in which we live, it will have served its purpose.

Conceptually, the life sciences are entering a phase of maturation. They have for long been able to get by with phrasing their propositions and problems in terms so general and indefinite that ample room was left for unsupported preconceptions. Yet, time has come when growing knowledge is forcing them to cease acquiescing in noncommittal symbolic cover terms for properties of living systems, such as "growth," "organization," "specificity," "metabolism," etc., and to go on to describe precisely and without equivocation the factual content of the phenomena thus labelled. And if one pursues this course judiciously, that is, without fear or favor—fear of violating injunctions imposed by the traditional dominance of a micromechanistic doctrine, or favor bestowed upon certain fashions of the day striving to fortify the status quo of that doctrine—one comes to the realization that the trend from naive microdeterministic causality toward macrodeterministic *"system"* theory is inexorable. The urge to fit our concepts to our expanding knowledge is breaking through the old conceptual constraints that tend to hold knowledge and understanding captive. To add to the momentum of this propitious trend in the life sciences, has been the principal incentive for my essay.

Yet, in order to document the much wider sweep and applicability of *"systems"* ideology and methodology, way beyond the narrow confines of my own essay centering on the life sciences, I have invited outstanding thinkers and practitioners from other areas to contribute supplements which would help in carrying the message across potential hurdles of incredulity and intellectual uneasiness. These supplements are independent individual contributions with a general focus on the human scene, but otherwise deliberately unprogrammed and without editorial attempt at cross-correlation. Accordingly, as one will note, they constitute a highly diversified medley of presentations—diverse in the nature and scope of subject matter; in the manner of treatment, ranging from the epigrammatic to the systematic; and in the degree of explicitness with which they spell out their bearing on the central theme of "hierarchic systems." But it is precisely this heterogeneity of kind of subject and manner of approach that makes the basic consonance of the statements, conclusions, and postulates so impressively compelling as testimonials for a growing universal recognition of the necessity, validity and utility of the "hierarchic systems" principle.

This booklet is thus a forward projection into what promises to become the basic thought structure of the future. In this sense, it is addressed primarily to those whose major stake lies in the future—the students of today. The Present, being the turning point from looking backwards to forward, has an obligation to introduce the student to the transition from the certainties of the past to the probabilities of the future. And in all probability, the wave of "systems" thinking sketched in this booklet will keep gaining in momentum. So, the student had better be prepared for it; particularly as it will leave in its wake a wider epistemological frame not only for the orientation of academic thinking and practical planning, but also for a deeper understanding of the indissociable inner connectedness of the world and of its rules of order. These rules, as primordial and firm as the law of gravitation, define the range within which man is free to move, politically and realistically—a frame with much wider latitude for the exercise of imaginative creativity than has as yet been put to work, but also with unalterable boundaries imposed by the natural stress limits beyond which organic systems would lose dynamic unity and disintegrate. In this sense, systems thinking carries a crucial sociological lesson —and indeed, mandate—for man to strive for harmony in personal and social life: to cultivate his creative powers to the utmost, but also to respect the rules of order, of give-and-take, inherent in the hierarchic systems principle of nature.

Although a book is by itself only a minor adjunct to the process of education, its meaningful interpretation to students by teachers and tutors can amplify its message to a high degree of effectiveness. Let me close, therefore, by pleading for a dual route for the message of this book to reach the student's mind—both directly and through the intermediacy of his preceptors.

I am immensely grateful to the illustrious group of contributors who have helped in giving the message, i.e., the plea for systems thinking, such solid factual support. My own essay, which follows, lays just some groundwork; their supplements have the virtue of clinching the argument by the convincingness of practical experience.

Table of Contents

The Basic Concept
Of Hierarchic Systems

A book is a means of communication—communication of information, of rules, of thoughts. Its tools are the symbols of language—numbers, words, terms. Tools in continual use tend to become blunted and need resharpening if they are to remain useful. Obsolete tools, unfit to serve new tasks, must be refitted or be discarded. Thus, tasks and tools must be kept in step in their developments.

Now, scientific language is the tool for the articulation of scientific knowledge and thought. To remain in step, thought and expression must stay linked. Their coupling, however, has reciprocal effects. On the one hand, refined knowledge forces advances in the language to express it, while, on the other hand, the habitual inertia of established language becomes, conversely, a drag on the further refinement of thought. Instead of enlarging and adapting our tools of expression to the demands of new insights into nature, we often, unwittingly, try to make nature, or rather our thoughts about it, fit into the narrow box of our traditional ways of representing it. Habits of language thus tend to mold habits of thought. For scientific knowledge to progress unhampered by such arbitrary constraint, its practitioners must concern themselves not only with the factual content of science, but with the adequacy of the intellectual and verbal tools used for communicating that content and for making it intelligible. If a scientific book is to be more than a catalogue of data, its writer must be mindful of that obligation.

This then is the rationale underlying the following outline of the conceptual tools and operations through which scientific knowledge is gathered, ordered, shaped and communicated. The intent is to bring these intellectual tools up to a standard of precision and cleanliness comparable to that taken for granted in the use of our technical tools. Being necessarily brief and sketchy, the outline cannot hope to overcome all the inertial residues of deeply ingrained habits of descriptive speech, which are not always based on equally deep thought. Yet, if it helps to set the stage for a better comprehension of the "principles of development", which are the object of this book, it will, partly at least, have served the purpose of the whole book: to present the reader with a framework for thinking about development, rather than with a mere recital of facts. The pedantic form in which the issues will be presented stems from purely pedagogical considerations.

I. WHAT IS SCIENCE? (Its aims and limitations)

Science is man's way of formulating for himself a mental replica of the Universe and all that is in it, in as complete, consistent and universally communicable form as is attainable to him through his senses, their extension by tools and logic, and rational ordering.

Its roots undoubtedly go back to the primordial need of all living beings to cope with nature—to exploit its vital offerings and to meet its fatal perils. Through the proficiency of evolution, each living individual is set out into the world not in blank innocence, left to learn to make its way precariously by experience, but on the contrary, well endowed with a fixed repertory of performances prepared without benefit of practice for the contingencies that nature holds in store. The measure in which this "instinctive" preknowledge about nature is subsequently enriched, expanded and refined varies, of course, enormously among different forms of life. But man is at the apex. Whatever rudiments of assessing nature his forebears may have shown, he alone owns in full measure the faculty of rational and systematic thinking about his place in nature and his relation to the Universe. Science is but the distillate of his knowledge about nature, gained methodically through his mental powers. By rationally supplementing and purifying his primordial instinctive notions and empirical observations about the Universe; by drawing cogent inferences from them to gain insight, understanding, and even foresight; by testing their validity in novel circumstances; and by articulating and communicating them through symbols of language; man has advanced from facts to concepts, from naïve registering of phenomena to critical interpretation of their interrelations and meanings, from information to knowledge.

This has been a process of steady maturation; we are still in the midst of it, the end is not in sight. Science has had a major share in its promotion; it also has reaped from it its share of benefits. However, different branches of science have matured at different rates. Physics leads in sophistication. Why do the life sciences lag behind? Without pretense at historical or philosophical profundity, the answer seems to lie in the head-start of physics in liberalizing the rules for acceptable theory. Biology, for long preoccupied with objects and phenomena accessible to direct inspection and rather unsophisticated exploration, had no occasion to question the explanatory adequacy of ordinary common sense and simple-minded concepts of causality, carried over from everyday life. By mental inversion of "seeing is believing" into "not seeing is cause for disbelief", it has fortified mechanical tangibility and logical plausibility in stations of monopoly in biological theory; whatever remained refractory to such explanation, was either ignored or discounted or exiled to extrascientific vitalistic territory.

By contrast, physical science has emancipated itself from

the restrictive hold on theory formation exerted by the credos of naïve plausibility and elementary causality. It has had to admit all logically compelling propositions and deductions, whether offending "common sense" or not, as long as the conclusions to which they lead can be validated by rigorous tests. Mathematically, such wholly "unrealistic" concepts as the square root of a negative number ($\sqrt{-n}$), or non-Euclidean space, have proved operational blessings to science; physically, the concepts of relativity, quantum theory, indeterminacy (Heisenberg), even thermodynamics with its disregard for the individual "elements" of a molecular population, are all signs of the conceptual rise of science above the naïve faith in simple causality. In short, the validity of a scientific concept is no longer decided by whether it appeals to "common sense," but by whether it "works."

There are two sides to this liberalized version of modern science, one sobering, the other exhilarating. The sobering aspect is that science has come to realize its limitations; that whatever we can hope to learn through science about the nature of the Universe, is limited by the range of human faculties and devices. This leads to the tantalizing conclusion that science can never attain the ideal of its infancy—"absolute truth"—but can only approximate to it asymptotically. The exhilarating vista, however, is the enormously widened range of opportunities which have opened up by the freeing of science from its former conceptual strait jacket of a naïvely conceived mechanistic naturalism. So much by way of preparation for what is to follow.

II. HOW DOES SCIENCE GO ABOUT STUDYING THE UNIVERSE? (In fragments)

Pragmatically, that is, in tending to the utilitarian satisfaction of his primitive biological needs, man, just like all animals, is not concerned with the Universe (or "nature") in its totality. He is concerned only with those features that either serve or harm him. By "instinct", i.e., evolutionary priming, or by deliberate self-confinement, he singles out those features and then ignores the rest. Since many of the biologically relevant features of nature recur persistently in the same assortments, clustered in configurations so uniform as to be recognized as definite shapes, odors, tunes, and so forth, man's mind comes to assign them special identities, —as "things" or phenomena, endowed with an existence of their own, wholly independent and separable from the variable and—to him—uninteresting context in which he meets them. And so his mind came to "abstract" some conspicuous and interesting fragments of the Universe—people, stars, rivers, flames, sand, song—, ignoring their enmeshment with the whole. His mind worked like a set of filters that passes only narrow bands of wave lengths from the total spectrum of radiations. His screening filters are the products of what his evolutionary past has sorted out, tested and validated as being of particular relevance to him, and everything else remains dim and blurred; that is, for man primaeval. The scientist, in setting the organism in contradistinction to its "environment", simply continues and reinforces that basic trait.

It is debatable whether, as has been sometimes stated, the new-born child, in a sort of abridged ontogenetic recapitulation of evolutionary history, perceives the outer world essentially as a mottled patchwork of colors, lines, sounds, and tactile sensations, from which only gradually his experience of "objects," as distinct from "background", emerges. Yet, the statement does reflect the fact that, as man's maturity and age increase, his powers of discrimination and judgement—his "filters"—gain in refinement. This enriches his experience with the recognition of more and more things and processes, but still leaves him with the impression that all of them can be conceived of as constant, independent entities, truly detachable from their "environ-

ment" or "background." But along with this process of ob-
jectivization, which is a sort of mental crystallization of
symbolic images, a contrary corrective process takes place:
the rigid notion of immutability yields to the recognition of
variability; that is, that things and events need not remain
ideally identical in order to retain their individual identities. They may fluctuate about some common state, or as in
ageing, change progressively and steadily. Acceptance of
change marks a further advance in man's sophistication,
for it signifies that he has added to his static notions about
objects a new dimension—time, implying change.

Soon he discovers that changes in one object or phenomenon often coïncide strikingly with changes in some formerly neglected sector of the "background"—plant growth,
with rain; sound, with vibration; a welt, with the sting of
a mosquito. And, if recurring with reasonable consistency,
what first was mere coïncidence, becomes linked together in
his mind as cause-effect chain. To test the premise, he re-
moves the "cause," and if thereafter the "effect" is missing,
he feels he has established the interdependence between
two otherwise independent entities. In fact, he has carried
out an experiment, instigated by keen observation and
shrewd conjecture. But what he pardonably disregards is
that he has not "removed" the "cause", but merely sub-
tracted its conspicuous share from the total, though less
conspicuous, account sheet of the state of the Universe.

For ordinary man, this disregard is a natural, sensible
and economic attitude; for science, however, the task arises
to look at the total. Science has to carry on where man's elementary and primitive mental operations leave off, even as
it uses very much the same strategy. Much like ordinary
man, it proceeds by observing, recording, comparing, sorting, rating, conjecturing; yet, it gives up man's anthropocentric orientation. It no longer lets itself be hemmed in by
the confines of man's self-interest; but it extends its sweep
to encompass the whole Universe. It no longer accepts auto-

matically and unchallenged the biologically-motivated primitive and prejudicial categories and ratings of common man and "common sense", but it subjects them to critical and clinical tests of their validity, consistency, and universal applicability. As a result, it can no longer concede true "independence" to the things that practical necessity had forced primitive man to classify and often personify, but on the contrary, it must go on to establish the range and degree of dependence which interrelates things and events with their context, erstwhile ignored as putatively unrelated. In short, it is science's task to restore to man's picture of the Universe the unity, consistency and continuity which his biologically well-founded primitive objectivations have obliterated. This is what we call scientific *synthesis.*

To be sure, this is just one of the directions of scientific probings. Efforts in the opposite direction, so-called *analysis,* have proved equally crucial and indeed more powerful. Analysis focuses downward, on ever smaller isolated samples of the Universe. In its descent, it encounters further compact packages of rather constantly recurring configurations—from organisms down to organs, cells, organelles, molecules, atoms, and subatomic particles. Each downward step involves a further degree of dismemberment of the primary unitary image of the Universe; involves cumulative abstractions due to either the disregard or the deliberate mental severance of those relational ties that link the abstracted "units" into the cohesive total fabric of the Universe. The success of this analytic method has been immense. It must not be forgotten, however, that its gains have to be bought at the expense of corresponding losses of information about the mutual relations between the "units" severed in the analytic process. This information needs to be restored when one climbs back up the scale in the synthetic direction, trying to fit things again together into original context. Note that the word "context" refers to "texture", or network, the nodal points of which had been given the status of independent isolated units by sheer abstraction. Yet, bear in mind that in reality they never have been, or could have been, truly isolated in the sense of separation from the continuum of the Universe. The whole notion of "isolation" is an abstraction.

"Isolation" and "independence" only connote that a unit —atom, molecule, cell, organism, etc., or what we then call an "object"—has been observed, imagined or actually made, to *shift* from one relation in the network to another without suffering in that shift any perceptible, detectable or significant loss of identity. "Perceptible, detectable, significant"—these three words at once bare our residue of subjectivity in our attempts to reconstruct a scientific picture of the outer world. Clearly, they are not attributes of a given object as such, but point to the subject who observes it: "perceptible" referring to our discriminatory acuity; "detectable", to the measuring and recording devices through which we potentiate our powers of discrimination; and "significant", to our special points of view and interest, which make the same phenomenon appear to us as highly relevant in one set of circumstances, and relatively negligible in another. As this phrasing indicates, we do indeed learn to take "circumstances," i.e., context, into account. Yet let us keep in mind that we do this not in terms of pure descriptive statements, but with admixtures of our own ratings, based variously on judgement, conjecture, intuition, or sheer convention. Description and evaluation are both key tools of the scientific process; but muddle and trouble are bound to resort from any scientific act that fails to distinguish between one and the other: between "what is there" (or "what we think is there") and "what we confer upon it" in the way of names, interpretations, valuations— projecting our biases into things of nature, and treating our *views* of them as if they were their *properties*.

Clean cognizance of this conceptual distinction has undoubtedly expedited the great modern upswing in the physical sciences. The life sciences, it seems, would stand to gain in both theoretical profundity and sharpness of experimental focus if they were to submit their conceptual vocabulary to a comparable audit. The following, by no means systematic, audit of some of the common terms current in biology is intended as a sample exercise in the indicated direction.

III. WHAT IS A UNIT? (An entity by abstraction)

A unit is a composite fragment of the Universe which in our experience has proved to retain sufficient identity over a given period of time to deserve a name—a conservative array of measurable properties amidst the continuously and erratically changing "background" phenomena that reveal no recognizable pattern. The period of assessment being left to our discretion, the life time of the valid definition of

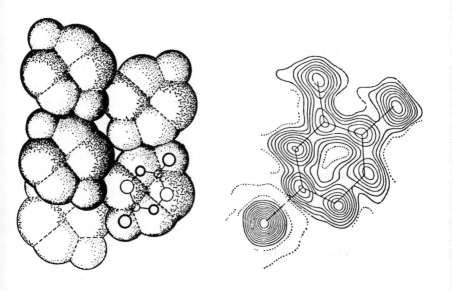

Fig. 1   Fig. 2

a given unit may be a millionth of a millisecond, as in elementary particles of physics, or many years, as in a higher organism, or billions of years as in a planet. Likewise, depending on how short or long we may choose to set our reference time span for observation, the unit may appear as either stable or variable, stationary or evolving. The chopping of the time continuum into periods (e.g., of development into "stages") is an expedient artifact. But so, let us remember, is the isolation and delineation of a "unit". For instance, unit molecules have been conventionally visualized and indeed represented in classroom models, as conglomerates of varicolored billiard balls, each standing for a subunit atom (Fig. 1). By contrast, modern knowledge has had not only to blend the subunits into continuous fields of electron clouds, but also to blur the former sharpness of the outer boundary of the molecule and let it melt into the surrounding molecular domains (Fig. 2).

Similarly, a living cell is not the neatly and stably delineated unit, suggested by the visual impression of the microscopic or electronmicroscopic picture of the dead and fixed object. But just as the subunits of the conspicuous outer cell membrane are held together by their molecular dynamics, so the dynamics of the whole cell unit extend way beyond that visible boundary, attracting and repelling molecules and ions from their surroundings according to electric charge and chemical affinities, sharp definitions dissolving into fuzzy halos. In the same sense, time demarcations setting off periods or stages, such as embryonic, fetal, postnatal, larval, adult, etc., should be viewed as grading into each other by transitions, rather than as bounded by discontinuities. Some such transitions may impress us as dramatic for their abrupt appearance and rapidity, but remember that "appearance" means merely the unveiling to our eyes of some event or object which has passed through a continuous line of preparatory developments proceeding steadily, but unnoticed.

The mode of thinking here expounded lays stress on continuity, as against fragmentation: undisrupted continuity of processes along the time line, as well as undivided continuity of interrelations and interdependencies among the putatively unrelated and independent units in space. Like islands, units must be conceived as interconnected, though not so solidly as by a bed of rock, but loosely by the all-pervading mesh of forces and interactions. Of course, if we confine our attention deliberately to a single unit, which as a useful analytical procedure is quite legitimate, then all effects that we see emanating from it appear to us as "actions." Yet, as soon as we widen our field of vision sufficiently, we recognize that all such actions, in reality, are *interactions*.

To place the concept of units of space and time into this widened perspective as a proper frame of reference, may provide a safeguard against the pitfalls of our habitual oversimplifying jargon, which speaks of genes as "units of heredity"; asks whether chromosomes or organelles are either "alive" or "non-living"; raises inclusions in living cells to the rank of "self-reproducing units"; and labels cells as either "differentiated" or "undifferentiated." (See below). Thus cautioned, let us then look more closely at what it is that makes a unit a unit.

IV. WHAT MAKES A UNIT WHAT IT IS? (Properties or designations?)

Above, a "unit" was characterized as a part of some larger complex, as being itself composed of parts, and having features that stand out by the consistency and persistence with which they occur in our experience. A unit is an item that tends to stay together and to retain its pattern when shifted in space, and to retain identity over a time span outlasting the fortuitous constellations of the moment. In short, its criteria are unity and conservation of pattern. All biological units being supra-elemental, that is, composed of sub-units, the problem of the unity of a unit resolves itself into the question of what makes the component subunits cooperate in such coordinated manner as to establish and preserve the rather definite pattern of the compound unit. That pattern may (a) show regularities of symmetry, polarity, or periodicity, as in a crystal; or (b) it may be a uniquely irregular array of parts, comparable to the letters in a word, as in the "coded" sequence of amino acid residues in a macromolecule of protein; or (c) it may be merely a standard pattern of behavior of the components that yields recurrently the same unitary result even though there is no geometric similitude among the constellations of the components from moment to moment.

One readily senses that there is a profound difference between classes (a) and (b), on the one hand, and class (c), on the other. All three must be assumed to satisfy the same thermodynamic postulate, namely, that the resultant higher-order unit represents a state of greater stability (or, in terms of statistical mechanics, of lower free energy content) than the sum of the component subunits if they were uncompounded. But the way this is achieved seems to be more firmly determinate in (a) and (b) than it is in (c). Whereas in the former, the components might be assumed to become stacked up or linked together by matching steric fitting, either by trial-and-error, as in a jigsaw puzzle, or by copying a pre-existing assembled model, (e.g., in the replication of a nucleic acid chain in a chromosome); in (c), the relative positions and constellations among the subunits are subject to almost infinite variations, which definitely rules out the mechanical precision of assemblage conceded to (a) and (b). That is to say, the high degree of regularity, or statistical constancy, which a (c)-unit as a whole displays on the *macroscale*, dissolves progressively as one descends analytically to the *microscale* of its components, whose individual behavior is far more irregular, erratic and unpredictable in detail, hence, offers decidedly an aspect of indeterminacy, or at least indeterminability, of individual microevents.

The impossibility of subsuming such (c)-units under the terms of resolutionist micromechanics, as seemingly can be done with (a) and (b), arouses a sense of intellectual discomfort, often leading to an instinctive aversion to the (c)–class of phenomena. As a result, biological theory (in contrast to physical theory) has tended either to deny the reality of that class, or to bypass it, or to try, by all sorts of artificial constructs, to squeeze it under the (a)–and–(b)-formula. Yet, it is so prominently inherent in all principles of development that it deserves special consideration in this place. Such (c)–units are properly called *"systems."*

V. WHAT IS A SYSTEM? (Not just a complex of greater complexity)

First, what is it not? It is not a haphazard compilation of items nor, at the other extreme, a complex of rigidly linked pieces or events, which automatically would put it under (a); for in either of those cases, the complexion of the total unit could still be predicted unequivocally from the information about its constituent parts, pieced together. In a system, we are faced with the opposite property, that is to say, the *state of the whole* must be known in order to understand the *coordination* of the collective behavior of its parts; or if one prefers to objectivize this proposition, one can express it in terms of "control" of the components by their collective state. The system as a whole has some characteristic conservative configuration which is maintained, not *through* a rigid concatenation of its component subunits, as in (a) and (b), but *despite the absence* of such internal interlocking braces.

This crucial difference can be revealed by a simple behavioral test. If a given interference with some subunits (by elimination, blockage or displacement) entails a corresponding deficiency or disfiguration of the total unit, the latter belongs in the (a) or (b) category; for instance, the blocking of a metabolic chain *in vitro,* the interruption of the sequence of consecutive steps in an instinctive behavioral performance, and the mutational effect of the deletion or alteration of a gene, would be in that class—perhaps not completely, but in essence. On the other hand, if a unit after a similar interference retains or regains its original state and configuration—its "equilibrium" condition—, it is to be rated as a system. A system could, therefore, be defined as a *complex unit in space and time so constituted that its component subunits, by "systematic" cooperation, preserve its integral configuration of structure and behavior and tend to restore it after non-destructive disturbances.*

Even though this is, indeed, the way a system is commonly characterized (e.g., in the following text, page *111*), it obscures some basic issues. The notion of "cooperation" is, of course, a useful and excusable relapse into the analytic mental artifact of "independence"; it really means that subunits, which always have been interrelated just *somehow,* now seem to follow common pattern—some *integral guidance.* If outside their systemic domain they displayed a high degree of freedom, this freedom has within the assembled state become severely restricted by restraints that can only be described in reference to all the members of the group. At every instant, the behavior of any one component unit is affected in unique fashion by the behavior of all the others, which to an outside observer, of course, gives the impression as if they all had a common aim—stability—and knew how to attain it. Whenever one group of components of the system deviates fortuitously, or is made to deviate, from its standard course too far in one direction, the rest automatically change course in the reverse direction so as to counteract the distortion of the pattern of the whole. But, one must ask, how do they come to know what happens everywhere and anywhere in their crowd and how do they manage to react appropriately? Since the number of possible departures from an ideal standard course is infinite, the number of corrective responses potentially called for from each component is likewise infinite, further compounded by the number of subunits involved in the collective response. Once faced straight on without hedging, this problem patently defies solution in terms of the "cooperation" of components assumed in analytic versions to be free and independent.

This is where a switch to the concept of *field continua,* as represented in figure 2 above, becomes wellnigh mandatory. Accepting the philosophical equivalence of the analytical corpuscular representation and the integral field portrayal of the outer world as two complementary points of view from which to look at the same reality, field theory seems definitely more adequate to describe system behavior for the following reason. If in a cohesive network in static equilibrium, e.g., a cobweb, one single thread is severed, the distribution pattern of strains and stresses in the whole fabric is altered, and a new equilibrium is attained, which is reflected in the changed positions and angles of the meshes. These measurable changes, therefore, give each element of the net the requisite clues (or, in a symbolic term, "information") about the direction and magnitude of its own vectorial displacement. Now, if a given thread, instead of being cut, were merely stretched, assuming that the system is elastic, obviously, in order for the whole system to be able to return to its initial configuration, each one of the other threads must "know" precisely what its own contribution to the total restoration process has to be: it must have registered its own passive displacement and, on release, move actively back by the same amount in exactly the reverse direction. And for a network of countless threads, which can be distorted in an infinite number of ways, this would seem to presuppose, as I said before, an infinitely high degree of "intelligence" on the part of the components. The absurdity of this anthropomorphic expression is, of course, self-evident. The truth is that the model simply appears to us as if it behaved intelligently (with "insight") because it typifies integrated systems dynamics in general, which we know most intimately from the intelligent performances of our brain.

A slight switch of viewpoint will make clear how the example of an elastic net can serve as simplified model for "systems behavior". By viewing the nodal points of the elastic net as sites of separate discrete subunits, formerly visualized as autonomous and independent entities, and letting the elastic threads stand for symbols of vectors in the dynamic field pattern of forces and "interactions" among the subunits, one attains at least a symbolic image of the conservative features of those integrated superunits which we call "systems". The case of networks whose meshes were severed, moreover, serves to illustrate how a system can transform from one equilibrium state into another without losing its systemic unity, identity, and integrity.

As far as it goes, the model is quite helpful in lifting our thinking out of the ruts of habitual micromechanistic preconceptions about the dynamics of biological systems without calling on supernatural principles for help. At the same time, it suffers from one fundamental weakness: It does not go far enough. In the first place, to make it more truly representative, one would have to enlarge immensely the relatively small number of component threads of the cobweb— let us say, to something like the almost astronomical number of cross-linkages among the molecules in an elastic rubber ball. On that scale, the distinction between virtual connections among discrete particles and field vectors (Fig. 1 vs. Fig. 2) becomes arbitrary and meaningless. But a far more serious limitation of the model is the fact that it is a *monotonic* system. That is to say, it displays systemic properties with regard to only a *single* modality of dynamics— that of mechanics. Its static equilibrium is a function of mechanical pressures and tensions, and its reactions are in response to such mechanical strains and stresses as are engendered by compressions, stretchings, shifts and shears, which distort its equilibrium pattern. No other modalities had to be considered, such as, for instance, cohesive forces, residing in chemical bonds and physicochemical properties; electric charge distributions; temperature gradients; and particularly, the interaction of disparate chemical processes centered in different parts of the net.

Yet, even the most elementary biological systems are *"polytonic"*, involving essential contributions from all of those additional properties. And even as each one of those disparate factors makes its contribution through its own peculiar dynamics, the system as a whole retains its integral unity of pattern as if by "cooperative" teamwork across the modal boundaries. For any living system to preserve its intact structure and operation, electric, chemical, hydrodynamic and—facultatively—thermal fluxes are vital. Therefore, the inequalities ("differentials") that generate them within the system (e.g., electric potentials, concentration gradients, sluice gates, and so forth) must be continuously sustained. Since to maintain them runs strictly counter to the thermodynamic tendency of equalizing differentials and homogenizing heterogeneous distributions, it goes without saying that the maintenance of a living system requires continuous input of energy (derived from the sun through food and its metabolic conversions). This is self-evident. But the most fundamental problem remains untouched: how is the available amount of energy so *channelled* in the system that *the combined effect of the various tributary forms will result in their conserving the integral state of the system as a whole conjointly?*

This question is perhaps the most pertinent paraphrase of the age-old question: "What is life?" The answer is not yet in sight. But from our recognition of the system character of organisms and their subunits, we can at least draw some lessons as to how not to ask the question and where not to look for answers. It seems, for instance, quite unreasonable to ask of any manifestation of a living system whether it is a mechanical *or* an electrical *or* a chemical process, for in reality, they appear always in conjunction and our ability to sort them into monotonic classes is merely due to our deliberate self-confinement to the use of correspondingly monotonic recording devices. By using ordinary photographic plates, one can, of course, reduce a colorful scenery to a monotonic scale of light intensities (gray shades). Similarly, by using strain gauges or potentiometers or spectroscopes, one can gather data about mechanical or electrical or chemical properties of a living system; but then to turn around and project the limited monotonic property of the recording instrument back into the studied object—comparable to inferring from a black-white photograph that nature is colorless—is an unpardonable, though not uncommon, somersault of logic. In fact, even if all the recordings gained by separate devices, each one monotonic in its kind, were pieced together by superposition, one would still get only an idea of the polytonic complexity of the object, but be no closer than before to understanding its system character; for a system, as explained above, has properties over and above those of a sheer complex.

Another lesson to be drawn from the adoption of the system concept in biological theory lies in the necessity of learning to distinguish empirically, as outlined above in point IV, between phenomena calling for the probabilistic thinking of network theory on the one hand, and phenomena that are amenable to the strictly deterministic treatment of linear reaction chains, on the other. Every living organism displays both kinds. In fact, the proper balance between both is one of the most vital aspects of organisms because on it depends the optimum combination of efficiency and adaptability. Symbolically, one could compare an organism to a wristwatch band, made up of rigid links coupled by springs, thus combining strength with elasticity. Gene replication, sequential metabolic chains, simple nerve-reflexes, the trigger action of fertilization, or the consecutive instinctive maneuvers through which a parasite identifies, approaches, invades, and exploits its host; these are all instances of rather rigidly determined programs, predesigned as chains of linearly seriated steps, each step linked solely to the one immediately preceding and the one immediately following, but with no direct regard to the integration of the whole performance. If the latter persistently turns out to be meaningful, credit goes not to any power of "insight" on the part of the components, but simply to the fact that the array of the pieces or steps had been *pre*programmed in the proper order by the evolutionary test of success. Since the measure of what we call success is viability, one cannot expect to find unsuccessful concatenations in members of a species that has survived. Therefore, if the many preformed blind chain-reactions in and of organisms add up to sensible performances, they owe this essentially to evolution's discriminative screening out of profitable combinations from a grab bag of historical trials.

The fact that such chain reactions offer a semblance of unity is, from the dynamic point of view, sheer coïncidence: they do not possess the intrinsic dynamic unity of true operative systems. Their kinship to automatons and puppets has endeared them to the analytical mechanists who, recognizing that such things can be dismantled, studied in pieces, and then put together again in working order, postulated that all living processes should ultimately be comprehensible in terms of similar chain reaction models. Such machine theories were often opposed—and in no less apodictic terms —by "holist" theories, which basically propagated a systemic point of view, referred to under such terms as "goal-directed", "homoeostatic", "self-organizing", and the like. Although both sides had valid arguments to offer in partial support of their tenets, the one-sidedness of their respective views made them become entrenched behind mutually exclusive doctrinal claims. It now seems clear, however, that by the verdict of unbiased study and judicious interpretation of organic nature, we must acquiesce in a split decision of the issue: to wit, that both sides have been right and that their claims are mutually compatible. When we look at cell behavior, or development, or nervous functions, we find that they are neither entirely in the class of unbroken linear "cause-effect" sequences, nor wholly the kind of self-adjusting operations denoting systems character. They are both, partly chains, partly networks at one and the same time.

Of the two, the latter appear to be more primordial, the evolutionary trend being to freeze secondarily as much of the free system dynamics into stereotyped chain reactions as is compatible with the preservation of that degree of systemic freedom essential for an organism to react adaptively to the vagaries of an unpredictable outer and inner world. Organic nature has learned to keep "institutionalization" within safe bounds; the rest remains systemic and adaptive. Consequently, any organic functions that are commonly referred to as "controls", "regulations", "compensations", and the like, come *prima facie* under suspicion of being instances of organismic system dynamics rather than of mechanisms with predesigned and ready pathway channels. In a systems operation, the appropriate response channels would form *ad hoc* as momentary manifestations of a primarily integrated response under some such over-all rule as "most economical maintenance of an ordered equilibrium state" or "attainment of a state of minimum free energy."

Unfortunately, matters are not that clear cut, for evolution has also provided organisms with some types of regulatory responses which even though they simulate systems behavior are definitely single-tracked predesigned mechanisms. They are constructed and operate essentially in the manner of thermostats or "homing" missiles, which "control" room temperature or their own flight course by "feedback" regulation. A pertinent example is the maintenance of constant blood pH through the monitoring device of the carotid sinus as sensor and its stabilizing "steering" of nerve impulses to respiratory organs. In cases of this kind, a closed circuit of chain reactions of proper design can be either demonstrated or presumed as a valid explanation. The circuitry may, for instance, consist of chains of neurons. Or it may be a chain of chemical messages, as in the coupling between different endocrine organs: for instance, pituitary gland and thyroid are so delicately pretuned to each other that the secretion of one can act as the specific signal for the other to increase or decrease the release, on its own part, of its preformed product, which then, in turn, acts back on the former as a governor of its discharges.

Successful computer technology is tirelessly devising and testing models of such physiological "feedback" control mechanisms, based on network circuitry, though not of the linear chain reaction kind. The scope of their applicability to life processes cannot yet even be guessed at. Yet it seems safe to state that their range is limited and indeed considerably short of offering the prospect of a *universal* model of system dynamics in organisms. There are both logical and factual reasons for this limitation. Logically, one must bear in mind that computers of whatever high degree of versatility are themselves products of an intelligent organic system acting with insight and foresight—the human brain. Having thus been predesigned for their tasks by a system, the proposition that computers might serve as *general* models of systems behavior is bound to end up as a circular and inconclusive argument. But even if this logical argument were to be disputed, there are incontrovertible factual objections to raising computers in rank from imitative to truly representative facsimiles of living systems. Those factual objections rest on the evidence that most of the fundamental organismic operations are carried on decidedly *without the benefit of predesigned circuitry.*

The reservation that this rejection of structural communication circuits might merely reflect our failure to have detected their presence can be countered by pointing to a large set of empirical data, such as the following. An individual's physiological functions, its populations of cell types, and each of the component cells itself, are all in constant flux, involving such an infinite amount of variability that no rigorously predesigned arrangements, whether based on structural linkages or on fixed patterns of positions and concentrations of chemical constituents, could survive undisrupted the incessant reshuffling. Yet, the cell, the population, the functional performances, and the total individual, all retain their identity, their integrity, their essential patterns inviolate. Moreover, they persist even after many artificial experimental interventions (further exemplified later in this book) specially contrived to upset any structural or compartmentalized provisions one might have conjectured to be prerequisite for a given ordered performance.

To be sure, definite "reserve performances," built into living systems by evolution, do exist. The faculty of regeneration, the "second wind" in breathing, blood clotting in a wound, fit perhaps into this category. It was only consistent on the part of preformationists, who adhered strictly to a machine-like concept of development, that upon seeing a *whole* embryo develop from each *half* of a bisected egg, they would presume each blastomere of the 2–cell stage to be endowed with a spare mechanism for the formation of a whole embryo, to be activated in just such an emergency as accidental blastomeral separation. What neither they nor evolution could have foreseen, was that enterprising human experimenters would move on in the opposite direction and fuse two whole eggs, with the result that a single harmonious giant embryo would form from the fused mass (see pp. 263 and 303). Since contrary to splitting, the natural occurrence of such a merger would be impossible, among other reasons because of the barrier of the enveloping egg membranes, it would have been absurd to postulate the providential inclusion by evolution of a spare mechanism for half an embryo in a whole egg. This once and for all disposed of the notion of spare mechanisms predesigned for developmental correctives, and by the same token, also of wholly rigid preformed mechanisms for the normal course of development as such.

We are thus compelled to fall back on pure and unreducible system behavior as an indispensable principle of developmental dynamics. Its irreducible characteristics can be briefly summarized as follows:

1.) Organic systems are units composed of smaller units subordinated to the system as parts or components.

2.) Organic systems are of heterogeneous composition, i.e., the components are not all of a single (monotonic) kind, but belong to distinct and discrete classes and kinds.

3.) The various populations of unit components themselves are not dispersed diffusely and intermixed at random, but show characteristic patterns of segregative and aggregative distribution, which can be mapped as the "field-pattern" of the system.

4.) This field-pattern tends to retain its configuration and unity during phases of stationary equilibrium despite the relatively free mobility of the component subunits.

5.) Upon enforced distortion or other kinds of disturbance well below destructive magnitude, the field-pattern tends to return to its former standard configuration.

6.) All these references to configuration pertain primarily to the patterned distribution of forms of energy (or forces) for which the ensuing and more readily discernible stable or stationary geometric constellations serve as indicators. Thus what we recognize as the form of a system must be regarded as the derivative manifestation of *formative*, or more precisely, "transformative," *dynamics*.

7.) Components of systems are often unit systems in themselves.

Living nature thus reveals itself to be ordered *hierarchically* in descending steps from supersystems through systems to subsystems, and so on down through different orders of magnitude and levels of systemic stability, with jumps through unstable conditions between levels. For instance, experiments have amply documented that a limb is not built in one act directly from its contingent of cells, but that cells in groups establish unit sub-limb structures (p. 253 and Fig. 48), such as a given skeletal element or a given muscle, that these in turn constitute limb parts (e.g., toes), and all of those then in concert yield integratively the unit limb. Descending from the level of the cell to its components, one notes the same type of a hierarchical scale: from cell to organelle (e.g., mitochondrion; chromosome; chloroplast granum; pigment granule; ribosome; sarcomere; cilium), to macromolecular system (e.g., ordered enzyme array; chromomere), to macromolecule (e.g., nucleic acid; lipoprotein); the units at each level displaying characteristic properties and patterns (e.g., standard compositions, shapes, sizes and functions) far more regular than their variable mutual relations.

The relative constancy of the order of a group as a whole as compared to the much greater variability among the constituent subunits, summarized in the preceding point, is one of the most crucial criteria, as well as tests, of true system dynamics. It permits us to express the character of a system symbolically in a simple formula, as follows ([3]). Considering that any given component, say a, is faced with a wide range of unpredictable fluctuations of its environment, which also includes the other components, $b, c, d, \ldots$

n, we must assume its reactions to cover a correspondingly wide range; let us designate that range as v_a, the variance of a. Similarly, the other components, *b, c, d, ... n,* have each their own range of potential excursions from the mean, i.e., variances v_b, v_c, v_d, ... v_n. At the same time, the total system preserves a high degree of *invariability*; that is, despite the seemingly erratic vagaries of its countless constituents, it does not fly apart. So, we can formulate this experience in an inequality according to which the total variance for the whole system, V_s, is infinitely less than the sum of the variances, v, for its aggregate components, or

$$V_s << \Sigma \ (v_a + v_b + v_c + v_d + \ldots\ldots\ldots\ldots v_n).$$

As one can readily perceive, this formula does embody the gist of system dynamics in terms of componentry; its realization would be impossible if the components were actually free and independent. In order to satisfy the formula, the components must be assumed to be so inter-meshed in a web of interdependencies that any excursion by any one of them, whether fortuitous or from applied force, is counterbalanced by the resultant of simultaneous excursions of all the others. Considering the infinite number of possible occurrences, one realizes that the representation of such an intricate network of delicately matched responses in terms of interactions among constituents conceived as basically independent is inferior to the concept of a field continuum. But since, as outlined earlier, both representations are equivalent and interchangeable in their portrayal of nature, the choice between them is rather a matter of taste or expediency.

Habits of thought, history and more advanced methodology have conditioned us to favor description in terms of separate quasi-independent entities in interaction with one another. Whenever feasible, we shall abide by this convention. This is legitimate as long as one bears in mind that it implies an abstraction and, furthermore, abstains from introducing additional illegitimate abstractions, such as imputing by careless idiom that the abstracted units can "act" or "do" or otherwise possess anthropomorphic spontaneity. All they can "do" is *inter*act with others. To lose sight of this verity, can lead to bizarre misconceptions in biology.

VI. WHAT IS ORGANIZATION? (The orderliness of the living state)

From a critical examination of the concept of "units" in Section IV, we have been led consequentially, in Section V, to the recognition of "systems" as a general category of nature. We can now proceed to focus more narrowly on those specific kinds of systems which are of prime concern in the framework of this book: the *organismic systems*. What is it then that makes them so special? A glib answer would be: *"Organization."*

Despite the common currency given to the term "organized" in dealing with biological objects and processes, its usage reflects mostly vague and varied notions rather than scientific rigor and precision. One often finds it used synonymously with "order" or "pattern" in general. But is it? If one tries to disentangle its manifold connotations, one arrives at some common core of meaning which, in the spirit here advocated, can be expressed in a formal probabilistic scheme. Rather than defining "organization" verbally, this scheme merely sets forth criteria by which to test when and when not the designation "organized" is appropriate for a given state of order.

Let us take two boxes A and B filled with five different kinds of components, s, e, n, o and v, in fixed proportions (Fig. 3). There are then three different states, X, Y, Z, in which the content can be arranged. These states differ by the probabilities of similarity or dissimilarity between samples taken, in one test, from different sites of the same boxes, and in a second test, from corresponding sites of different boxes. We shall refer to reasonably large standard samples taken from sites C_1 and C_2 of box A as A_1 and A_2, respectively, (equally for B, as B_1 and B_2). The probability that the contents of two samples will be essentially alike, varies with the particular state of order. Pairs of samples that are practically equivalent will be indicated by the equality sign; probabilities of major dissimilarity, by an inequality sign.

The most uniform distribution of content at random is represented in state X, all samples being essentially the same ($A_1 = A_2 = B_1 = B_2$). This signifies an ideally homogeneous mixture of a heterogeneous population, or maximum disorder. State Y is characterized by the segregation of groups of homologous components within a mixed population; different species are sorted out in different locations, like-to-like. This step away from total disorder is a necessary, but not sufficient, criterion of organization; it is insufficient in that there is no similitude between the *patterns* of distribution of the segregated species in A and B ($A_1 \neq A_2 \neq B_1 \neq B_2$). This state Y might be referred to as *manifest,* but *unpatterned,* complexity. The next step of ordering then leads to Z, which in its typically *patterned complexity* reveals the most pertinent connotation of organization: *similitude between the overall* patterns of individual systems ($A_1 = B_1; A_2 = B_2$) in conjunction with *disparity among the samples within each system* ($A_1 \neq A_2; B_1 \neq B_2$).

Accordingly, if we now visualize A and B as two cells of the same type or as two individuals of the same species, we gain at once a realistic view of the nature of organization in living systems, based on a probabilistic concept of similitude, instead of on the deterministic fiction of tin soldier-like identity. If, in the simplest case, state Z, for instance, represents a living cell with baso-apical differentiation, state X corresponds to its homogenate, and Y to the artificial separation of the latter into fractions by different incongruous methods. Or, on a higher level, if X symbolizes a

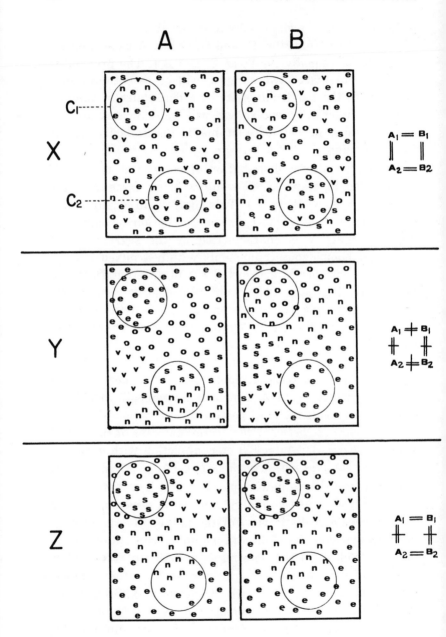

Fig. 3

scrambled mixture of individual cells of different types, obtained by dissociation of a normal organ, then Y would depict the "self-sorting" of like cells according to tissue type ("histiotypic" reassembly), while Z would connote an additional step yielding the reconstitution of a complete organ of morphologically and physiologically typical features of composition, proportions, form and function. The empirical fact that the emergence of both Y and Z from X has actually been witnessed in experimental tests, strengthens the pertinence of our models for the distinction of *degrees of order*, with "organization" as the highest.

Although the models of Figure 3 illustrate *spatial* organization, it should be pointed out in passing that they can be readily converted to descriptions of organization in *time* as well. In the place of boxes we then set time-periods so that the letters which stood for bits of box-*content* now signify elementary *processes*. In X, these processes would follow each other in completely haphazard sequence, like rows of letters picked out at random from scrambled printing type; in Y, selected arrays of letters would appear clustered, but quite unsystematically; whereas Z would represent sequences of "words". While this does not seem to be the place to dwell on the possible significance of such a model of kinetic organization of processes in definite chronological patterns, it might be indicated to mention at least the possibility that the "coded" sequences of energy pulses from such series might, like a Morse code, serve as signals to activate corresponding systems keyed or tuned to them, comparable to the selective reception by resonance of messages in radio broadcasts.

Having attempted in this section to give some sharper definition to the concept of "organization" than is implicit in its various purely literary versions, it remains to call attention to one further ambiguity of language apt to introduce confusion. A common example is the term "adaptation", which refers both to the *act of becoming* adapted and, in a more general sense, to the *state of being* adapted, regardless of whether this state of fitness has come about by actual fitting or by sheer happenstance. Similarly, the term "organization" is being applied indiscriminately at one time to the dynamics of an actively ordering process, of which the final ordered arrangement is the direct result and indicator, and at another time, to any ordered array that satisfies our model, even though it may have been pieced together from separate processes running side by side without mutual pattern-related interactions. We need only return to comments made earlier (p. xxviii) to recognize that living beings confront us with both of these two forms of "organization"—a genuine one based on integrative free system dynamics, and a simulated one of evolutionary origin, in which the product is preordained as a mosaic of processes, the combination of which happens to have proved in past experience to be fit and viable.

This dual meaning disposes of the age-old antithesis in embryology between epigenesis and preformation; development, as will be shown in the text, is a mixture of both (see p. 402 f.). One recognizes this dual character in all the formative and differentiative processes which underlie morphogenesis. Some of those processes interact freely in truly systemic coordination, while others are linearly linked seriatim in rigid sequential order. The former admit of various degrees of latitude in the rates and successions of phases, letting identical integrated results be attained by many diverse routes, while in the latter any rearrangement in the time schedule of steps stops the whole process in its track (save for certain instances in which evolution has provided a bypass, equally linear, for just such an emergency disruption). Some pertinent examples are cited in the text.

The chronological patterns of all living systems display this duality of principles of operation. Each component phase may, taken by itself, be a rigorously predesigned chain reaction (e.g., a metabolic cycle; a linear sequence of hormonally triggered developmental and metamorphic stages; a neural chain reflex). Yet evidently, a sheer assembly of such linear chains would never yield a reasonably harmonious total performance if their individual kinetics were truly of clock-like microprecision; for the incessant erratic fluctuations of their various local microenvironments would preclude their proceeding as a group *in concert*. They would end up in chaos, unless there were coordinating interactions to slow the racers and to speed the laggards commensurately; and that presupposes system behavior.

Three practical examples from different levels of the biological hierarchy may help to illustrate this fundamental point. In any diagram of the network of chemical interrelations in a basic metabolic system of the cell, one recognizes not only linear sequences, but also many branchings, anastomoses, cycles and alternative routes, all interlaced in an integrated master system operating through subsystems, as well as chains. At the opposite end of the hierarchical scale, we find the eco-system of a given geographic region as a paradigm of the principle of interdependencies, partly prestructured, partly in free systemic interaction, which make it possible for organisms to mesh harmoniously with their environment and with one another, both individually and in groups, so as to exist, persist and thrive.

The third example (fig. 4) is chosen from an intermediate level, germane to the context of this book. It is a diagram of the web of processes thus far identified as tributaries to what, in a cover term of deceptive simplicity, we call "the development of the nervous system." ([4]) Some of the arrows are explained in the chapter on Neurogenesis; others are known, but only spottily investigated; still others, although studied more widely, are still poorly understood. Since there undoubtedly are many more that have not yet been revealed at all, we must regard this picture of the

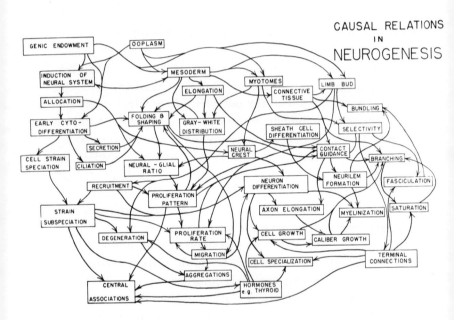

Fig. 4

maze of interactions as incomplete and greatly oversimplified. Even so, just contrasting this manifold with its unified finished product—the functional nervous system—and contemplating further that, in fact, every one of those plain arrows hides under its simple appearance a very complex set of operations, one begins to grasp the essence of the basic problem of development: how can an egg in a standard, yet fluctuating, environment, ever manage to yield a harmonious mature organism of typical and unified "organization," if that end is reached not by a simple bunch of strands of reaction chains, but through a maze of innumerable intersecting pathways, each varying in some unpredictable degree according to the local circumstances of the moment? The demonstrable reality of that variability *en route* defies any attempt to fall back on a concept of machine-like microprecision as explanation of developmental order, and by the same token, makes the recourse to system theory compelling.

VII. WHAT DISTINGUISHES AN ORGANISM FROM THE SHEER SUM TOTAL OF ITS PARTS? (Is it a matter of "information"?)

According to the criteria outlined in the preceding section, an organized system differs from its scrambled parts neither in mass nor weight nor content nor any other properties of its separate components, as far as these can be determined apart from their enmeshment in the whole ensemble. The critical difference, therefore, is not one of matter but one of the *pattern of relations* among the components. The salient feature of the "organized" state is that the overall features of this pattern are essentially invariant, whereas the behavior of the components varies greatly in detail from case to case and from moment to moment (see p. xxxiv). For example, limb buds develop into limbs essentially alike in their finished form, even though the detailed courses taken by the formative mesenchyme cells in their

growth and movements are different and unique in each individual case. The same applies for the subcellular range in
regard to the cell as a whole, the behavior of the cell being
far more invariant and predictable than are the vagaries of
its constituent organelles and macromolecular clusters; and
so on down the orders of magnitude on the hierarchical
scale of organization. A presentation of the course of development that ignores, bypasses or misrepresents these empirical facts of the attainment of a developmental product
of typical order despite a high degree of indefiniteness of
the activities of the components is spurious, and any allu-
sive wording that tries to conceal the fact of macrodeter-
minacy without stereotypy of the underlying performance
is not just meaningless, but scientifically irresponsible.

Having said this, let me at once turn to the components
of the inner sanctum of every organism—the genes and the
material counterparts of those symbolic units, the corresponding stretches of the deoxyribonucleic acid double
helix. I am taking for granted that the reader is familiar
with the essentials of the dramatic progress made in molecular genetics, and on a minor scale, developmental genetics.
What is of concern in the present context is only the question what that progress has been able to contribute to the
elucidation of the problem of developmental *organization,*
and indirectly thus to biological organization in general, in
analytical terms. To this question an honest and informed
answer can only be an unqualified "nothing."

To be sure, the list of gene-related "characters" of a
developed organism has grown to the point where it seems
more appropriate to question whether there would be any
character germane to an organism that is *not* gene-related
But let me stress the semantic distinction I am introducing
here between "gene-related" and "gene-determined", as the
nexus is usually called. Similarly, my placing "character"
in quotation marks is based on a similar semantic reservation, for what we commonly label as a "character" has

really no independent existence of its own but refers to a *differential* between two systems that has forced itself on our attention; most such differentials in fact going unnoticed and remaining undetected. They thus refer in linguistic terms to differences in the attributes of a subject noun, and if the latter is endowed with the property of organization, it would be a curious somersault of logic to impute organization itself to be no more than the sum total of attributes. The same argument then applies at the other end of the relationship to the genes, for what we are actually testing is an unequivocal correspondence between the *differences* among certain terminal attributes ("characters") of a developed system, on the one hand, and *differences* between the corresponding genomes, on the other. We thus come to relate legitimately a gene differential to a corresponding differential of characters. What we are apt to forget, or at least by our shorthand language to obscure, is that neither the genes nor the characters have existed in isolation as autonomous entities but have formed parts of an organized system, the order of which remains a problem *sui generis*.

The primacy of the organized state of a living system thus becomes axiomatic, and there is nothing in our practical experience in cellular and developmental biology that would justify the illusion that freely operating genes can be the "source" of organization of the developing system in the sense of imposing order *de novo* on an extra-genic matrix not already in possession of an organization of its own. Yet, this is precisely the illusion created by the thoughtless and careless use of the term *"information"* rampant in current literature and as misleading as a mirage in the desert. Instead of a straightforward and honest profession of ignorance as to just what the relation might be between a given genic alteration and a correlated developmental phenomenon, for instance, in morphogenesis, or even a peculiar functional manifestation of a developed organ, such as the brain, we just read the glib statement that "the genic information has been transferred or transmitted to that terminal product." In a benevolent interpretation one might pass such a statement as an expression of faith that genes can actually create order from chaos, although the conclusion is untenable on both logical and factual grounds. But other than this, that phraseology serves only as a smoke screen, concealing the real problems and distracting from the pursuit of realistic research. In its abuse as cover-term for *lack* of concrete information, the term "information" is a misnomer, evidently based on a naïve misapplication of the principles of valid information theory. Let us look briefly at the facts.

Information theory deals essentially with the rules of order in meaningful non-random constellations of groups of diverse elements (in the case of linear series, the sequence). The standard analogy is the typical seriation of letters in a word. Such order can then act as "code", capable of serving as model for arraying an erstwhile disordered mass of elementary units into a matching configuration. In this manner, vaguely reminiscent of the method of the printing press, the serial order of the DNA molecule is perpetuated in the replication of the molecule during growth, parts of the series then serving as informative models for the serial order of elementary nucleic acid residues in the transcription of genic sequences to ribonucleic acid (RNA) words, the serial order of which is then translated, or copied, as it were, into a correspondingly specific stringing up of amino acids into polypeptide chains, prefabricated building blocks of proteins. All this is straightforward perpetuation of a given degree of order in strict accordance with precepts of information theory. It involves a commutation of existing order rather than the creation of new sets of order on a higher integrative level.

The secondary and tertiary foldings of the proteins into three-dimensional conformations, being entirely predetermined by the primary arrays, are likewise simply conversions of "information", preexisting in the chains, into overt transfigurations. The resultant pattern of the protein units often predisposes them to polymerize with equal units into linear or even three-dimensional pseudo-crystalline arrays. But those form rigid structures which do not satisfy the postulate of almost infinite degrees of freedom in detail of behavior left to the componental interactions of member units of a higher organizational system, such as a cell, an organ, or an organism. Nor do the enzymatic functions acquired by many of those proteins by virtue of their conformation yield any clues to the emergence of such higher systems of morphogenetic order except in interaction within an already established frame of organization which could explain why an indiscriminate mixture of enzyme and substrate molecules would lead to locally segregated and chronologically ordered manifestations.

The question thus remains how to get from an incredibly diversified scramble of molecular activities to the integrated overall systemic order of the cell; from the imprecise courses and variable performances of individual cells to organs which are so infinitely more similar among the members of a given species than are the detailed componental performances of their unit members in morphogenesis; or even how to explain how this same cell group in a limb bud can form in one case the asymmetric pattern of a right limb and, in another case, in response to some environmental alteration, produce a structure of exactly the opposite asymmetry ([5]). It is in entering the domain of these problems that a concept of "information transfer" breaks down, much as a railroad train on tracks that suddenly end in a sandy wasteland, beyond which lies the point of destination, will never get there; or rather could get there only if at the end of the pre-set linear guidance along the tracks, free navigation across the intervening trackless space, steered by systems dynamics, takes over. In other words, what appeared as an unstructured space is not truly a wasteland, but is a system in which the role of linear mechanical tracks is performed by the guiding cues of the dynamic field structure of the total complex.

In the more than fifty years of my intimate preoccupation with the phenomena and problems of morphogenesis, during which I have been shuttling back and forth from organisms through their organs, tissues, cells, and cell components, to the molecular orders of magnitude and back on up, I have been unable to find a way of deriving, free from all preconceptions, a comprehensive and realistic description of the developmental process otherwise than by reference to a dualistic concept, according to which discrete units (molecules, macromolecular complexes, cells, or cell groups) are enmeshed in, and in interplay with, an organized reference system of unified dynamics of the collective of which they are the members. In passing, I might mention that conceptually, this field-element dualism might be compared to the field-particle complementarity in physics. I have dealt with this problem, and especially its bearing on the concept of "genetic determinism", in a recent book, to which readers interested in the theoretical foundations of the principle might be referred ([6]). For the student of developmental dynamics, it remains simply an empirical fact. I note with satisfaction that my advocacy of the field concept is to this day not only shared, but increasingly reasserted by authors thoroughly familiar and closely identified with the study of the role of genes in development [e.g., 7, 8].

In conclusion, the term "morphogenesis" (translated to "origin of form") must not be interpreted to mean origin of organization. It merely signifies the transformation of organized *dynamic* patterns (fields) of a continuum of matter into *overt* patterns through interaction with discrete unit components: the effects of these interactions become manifest as progressive diversification among cell lines, cytodifferentiation, oriented movements of cells, differential growth, change of shape, emergence of novel groupings, acquisition of new functional faculties, and so forth. Unquestionably, there would be less room for misconception if instead of referring to developmental dynamics as "formative", we were to designate them as "transformative", for then the notion that order or organization as such are created *de novo* within a totally random pool of unit elements could not arise. That notion is definitely implicit in much of current biological theory, regardless of whether one chooses to consider the emerging order as ordained by a prestigious act of "informational instruction" from the genome within, or by a supernatural intervention of an "entelechy" from without. For all practical purposes, it will suffice to bear in mind that the developmental system is a "system", in which the genes do not "act" as independent autonomous dictators, but with which they simply "interact" as cooperative parts.

VIII. SUMMARY ("Molecular and cellular ecology" of the living system)

Let us then turn from more or less figmental notions of genes as being the monopolistic sources of developmental order to a more accurate, "bipartisan," description of their role in development. Viewed in a realistic light, they do not generate order but are crucial converters in bringing latent order to overt expression. The diagram of Fig. 5 is a schematic picture of the dynamic scenery in which developmental dynamics operates. It portrays the unitary system of an individual higher animal (referred to as "organism" for short) as consisting of a hierarchy of inscribed shells of subsystems of progressively lower orders of magnitude. Let us disregard the many simplifications of the model; for instance, the omission of sub-systems within the cell other than the nucleus (e.g., organelles). Each shell is character-

ized by certain special properties or material possessions up
and above the sum total of the enclosed sub-systems. The
only constituent in this hierarchy to which we must
concede micro-precision of a high degree of minute structural order are the genes innermost. The rigidity of this
micro-precision exempts the genome from the designation
as a system, for it lacks the degree of componental latitude
outlined in Section V as diagnostic for a system. The same
exemption applies to the processes of gene replication and
of the step-wise information transfer that defines the composition and configuration of proteins and of those other
macromolecular assemblies specified by proteins with enzymatic functions. However, it no longer applies at the next
higher level of the cell.

At that level, the rigid concatenation of "information
transfer" in which products, shaped after models, serve, in

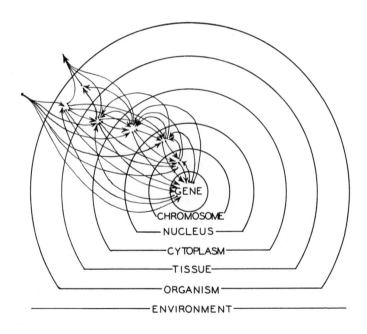

Fig. 5

turn, as models for consecutive steps of synthesis, dissolves into a far less stereotyped mode of operation. And if left to interact freely, the highly diversified populations of molecular compounds of the cell content would only yield maximum thermodynamic disorder. As long as it is alive, the living cell patently defies such thermodynamic "death". Scientifically speaking, this reveals that the heterogeneous population of molecules that constitutes a living cell does not have the unlimited degrees of freedom of interaction that it would have in the dispersed state of thermal agitation in a test tube solution. In short, molecular group behavior on the level of the cell is neither as micro-precisely programmed as are the steps up to proteins nor is it as devoid of pattern as one would expect from a plain mixture of the very same molecules outside the living cell. Evidently, the physical parameters of the intact cell constitute a dynamic framework which enables different species of the molecular population to aggregate or segregate, as the case may be, in separate chemical domains, similar to the scheme in Fig. 3Z. The dynamics involved reminds one of the principles of ecology, according to which living beings on earth occupy niches in characteristic patterns of mutual relations determined by each ecosystem as a collective unit.

Based on this analogy, I have proposed a concept of "molecular ecology" ([9]) as a prime object for the study and comprehension of the living cell; as one can readily see, this is essentially another version of the systems concept. The typical organization of the community pattern of the molecular population of a cell, as expressed in the symbol of molecular ecology, distinguishes the living cell from its homogenate,—a distinction which ought to serve as the acid test for the various notions of a cell we carry in our minds and frequently project into our conclusions and expressions. Even where, in a cell, some relatively stable structural assemblies, such as fibers or membranes, might look at first sight like solid straws to which hopes for mi-

cro-mechanical structural backbones and partitions might
cling, experience tends to show that quite the reverse is
true, namely, that those structures owe their existence to
special local conditions of the dynamics of molecular interactions, which may prevent free assembly of molecular
units in any but a given linear direction (in the case of
fibers) or favor recruitment and planar arraying of selected molecular species along an interface (in the case of
membranes). Molecular ecology transcends the biochemistry of isolated reactions in the same sense that ecology
gives information way beyond what could be extracted
from even the most complete systematics of animals,
plants, and microbes; or in another simile, in the sense that
a poem or even a simple message cannot emerge from a
random selection of words from a dictionary.

REFERENCES

1. Weiss, Paul. Knowledge: A Growth Process. Proc. Amer. Philos. Soc. *104:* 242-247, 1960.
2. ———. *Dynamics of Development: Experiments and Inferences.* Academic Press, New York, 624 pp. 1968.
3. ———. The Cell As Unit. J. Theoret. Biol., *5:* 389-397, 1963.
4. ———. Nervous System (Neurogenesis.) In: *Analysis of Development.* Eds.: B. H. Willier, Paul Weiss, and Viktor Hamburger, Saunders Co., Philadelphia, 346-401, 1955.
5. Harrison, R. G. On Relations of Symmetry in Transplanted Limbs. J. Exp. Zool. *32:* 1-136, 1921.
6. Weiss, Paul. *Life, Order and Understanding: Three Variations on a Common Theme.* (In Press—Texas Univ. Press).
7. Waddington, C. H. Fields and Gradients. In: *Major Problems in Developmental Biology.* Ed.: Michael Locke, Academic Press, New York: 105-124, 1966.
8. Hadorn, Ernst. Dynamics of Determination. In: *Major Problems in Development Biology.* Ed.: Michael Locke, Academic Press, New York: 85-104, 1966.
9. Weiss, Paul. Differential Growth. In: *Chemistry and Physiology of Growth.* Ed.: A. K. Parpart, Princeton University Press: 135-186, 1949. (Reprinted in Reference 2.)

The Ecosystem
Level of Organization

HELMUT K. BUECHNER
Office of Environmental Sciences
Smithsonian Institution, Washington, D.C.

An ecosystem, as Paul Weiss has pointed out (p. 31), is a "paradigm of the principle of interdependencies, partly prestructured, partly in free systems interaction, which make it possible for organisms to mesh harmoniously with their environment and with one another, both individually and in groups, so as to exist, persist and thrive." It reflects the dualistic concept of systems in which discrete units are "enmeshed in, and in interplay with, an organized reference system of unified field dynamics of the collective of which they are the members" (p. 38). The discrete units in ecosystems are individual organisms, and their interplay emerges in populations and communities as subsystems, as well as in the dynamics of the ecosystem as a whole. The concept of an ecosystem as one end of a spectrum of hier-archically organized systems of increasing complexity, from atoms upward, provides an indispensible tool for understanding how nature, including man, is structured and how it works. In the present article an endeavor is made to apply the concepts of systems to the ecosystem level of organization.

First of all, it is important to understand more clearly the meaning of ecosystem in the context of this discussion. The term can be used legitimately to refer to any level of organized system, from cells to biocommunities, when the total environment is included with the network of units and their interactions. In other words, by including the environmental matrix in which the network is enmeshed as part of a system, one conceptualizes an ecosystem. This is a logical approach, since no living unit, or network of units, survives except in an environment, which is as much a part of the system as the integrated network of units and their interactions. This broad concept of an ecosystem underlies all discussions of the higher-order systems from the population upward.

It is necessary also to distinguish an ecosystem as the highest level of hierarchically organized systems to provide a concept and a term for discussions at this level. In common currency an ecosystem is thought of as the integration of the communities of living organisms and their total non-living environment in a geographical region of the earth at a particular point in time, and this is the concept referred to in the present discussion. An ecosystem has no particular size, and its boundaries may not be distinct when one trans-lates the concept to observable reality in nature. The selec-tion of an operational system for research or management depends more on convenience than on rigid definitions. One may speak of "major" ecosystems in various geographic regions of the earth—such as tundra, tropical rainforest, deciduous hardwood forest, coniferous forest, grasslands, marine estuaries, or deserts. These terms evoke the concept of ecosystems, despite the apparent inadequacy of the labels which focus on vegetation to the exclusion of animals. It must be borne in mind also, that a major ecosystem embraces many subecosystems as component parts of the larger whole in any given geographical region.

Conceptually, the irreducible units of the higher levels of biological organizations in the three-dimensional network are the individual living organisms. They form the nodal points of the network, and their interactions form the strands of the network. The network is enmeshed in, and integrated with, the environmental matrix; and the whole forms a population, community, or ecosystem. Symbolically, the individual organisms may be considered the irreducible units for systems above the organismic level, in a manner comparable to subatomic particles at the elemental level, and one can envision a field-organism complementarity similar to that of the field-particle complementarity in physics. At the atomic level, only about 50 subatomic particles are involved in the formation of about 100 chemical elements, which in turn form only a few thousand naturally occurring simple molecules. Living organisms are based on about one-fourth of the elements, and a relatively small number of simple molecules are involved in the elaboration of macromolecules. At the ecosystem level some 5 to 10 million different species are involved, and within a single species most of the members are genetically different from all the others. Thus the complexity of the field-organism complementarity at the ecosystem level is incomparably greater than that of the field-particle complementarity at the atomic level, and when one integrates the human mind with an already incredibly complex nonhuman ecosystem, it becomes apparent that the contemporary world ecosystem is not only more complex than one thinks it is, but more complex than one can think. An approach through hierarchically organized systems, on the other hand, enables one to comprehend significantly a great deal about the structure and functioning of the total ecosystem and its subsystems.

As a specific illustration of the complexity of ecosystems, consider Oxford University's estate at Wytham Woods, where Charles S. Elton studied the animal communities intensively for more than a quarter of a century. Here a rich pattern of open fields, limestone outcroppings, woodland, springs, and marshes is set in riverine surroundings. The complexity of this pattern of ecosystems within an area of about two square miles can be appreciated from the diversity of animal life, which includes an estimated 5,000 species, about 3,800 of which have been identified. To the animals one must add numerous species of plants and microorganisms that are also essential components of the ecosystems at Wytham Woods. Each species is represented by populations varying from a few individuals, for some of the rarer plants and larger mammals, to billions, for some of the microbes. Thus, on an individual basis, the number of interacting component units of living organisms in the system's network is astronomical, and the interplay among the organisms in their environmental context staggers the imagination.

Out of an incredible scramble of interactions between individual organisms, patterns of structure and processes emerge as integral configurations of populations, communities, and ecosystems. To begin with, the individuals of the same species in a given area at a particular time constitute an intraspecific local population with emergent attributes that reflect the collective behavior of the individuals —including natality, mortality, intrinsic rate of natural increase, sex and age structure, social behavior, social organization, and self-regulating mechanisms of numerical control. To persist within the ecosystem the population must maintain homeostatic stability from year to year. At a given season of the year the average number of individuals per unit area, or density, is remarkably similar to that of the previous year in most species, irrespective of the vicissitudes of weather conditions, variations in factors causing mortality, and other vagaries in factors that affect the increase or decrease in numbers. Explosions in populations, as in locust outbreaks, sporadic marine algal blooms known as red tides, deer irruptions in developmental stages of vegetation change, or the current human population, are exceptional phenomena of populations associated with major perturbations to the ecosystem. Periodic fluctuations in some animals such as the lemming, snowshoe hare, and ruffed grouse may represent adaptations to ecosystems of harsh climates at high latitudes, in which a wide amplitude in the steady-state system has survival value.

Numerical homeostasis can be achieved through a variety of physiological and behavioral processes. Natality in population of white-tailed deer can vary through the number of ova released, the number of live births, and the minimum age at first conception. Under favorable environmental conditions, particularly with regard to food supply, about half of the females become pregnant while they are fawns, and the average number of offspring is more than two per female, whereas under poor nutrition fawns rarely breed, and the average number of offspring is less than one per female. In populations of elk the flexibility in natality is more restricted, since females have only one young at a time, but natality increases under favorable conditions through breeding of 50% or more of the yearling females, which would otherwise delay breeding until the age of 2½ years. While nutrition undoubtedly plays a major role in the regulation of natality, other more subtle interactions may be important, such as the psychology of crowding or territorial behavior. In the Australian magpie territoriality has been shown to regulate natality, and a large floating population in less favorable habitat harbors a high percentage of nonbreeding females. Although supporting evidence is still extremely limited, social behavior appears to be one of the most important population-regulating mechanisms among many of the higher forms of animal life, particularly in birds and mammals, functioning through natality or mortality, or both. Changes in a population's pool of genetic variation, at periodic high density in some species of small mammals, may provide a mechanism for numerical regulation. Parasitism or predation may play the dominant role in the regulation of some insect populations. Whatever mechanisms are involved in homeostatic regulation of numbers, a population must adjust to the total ecosystem through the intrinsic interplay of its members and through extrinsic interplay with its total environment, if it is to survive as a component of an ecosystem. These self-adjustments of the population emerge from the field dynamics of the system, as determined by the collective, seemingly "intelligent," behavior of the member organisms. Furthermore, numerical recovery from exceptionally low levels is a manifestation of the resilience of population systems in returning to the original form following nondestructive disturbances, and confirms the integrated systems behavior of populations. Thus it is logical to conceptualize populations as systems at a higher order, next to and above that of the organismic level.

The interplay between populations of closely related species determines a niche structure, or spectrum of ways of life, through which competition for life requirements is reduced or excluded within an ecosystem. Five congeneric species of insectivorous warblers, for example, are able to coexist and nest in the same spruce forest, by dividing up the resources of the ecosystem in such a way that each species is limited by a different factor—different resources, the same resources at different times, or the same resources at different places—through unique patterns of behavior. Two of these species of warblers depend upon periods of superabundant food, while the others depend upon differences in feeding positions and nesting dates to reduce competition, and the overall effect is that each species inhibits its own population more than it does the populations of the other species. Similarly, slight differences in food habits, utilizing different grasses, the same species at different seasons, or different portions of the same species of grass, enable a spectrum of 10 to 20 species of ungulates to coexist and efficiently utilize the savannas of eastern Africa.

Niche structure emerges from the interplay between populations of different but closely related species, and provides an insight as to some of the mechanisms underlying speciation, and the formation of communities of population systems of two or more species, and ultimately of whole ecosystems. Communities form more complex higher-level systems above intraspecific populations, with emergent properties not found at the lower levels of organized systems. In terms of observable structure, the physiognomy of terrestrial vegetation provides an excellent example of integral configurations at the community level. The layering of community systems as canopy, understory, and ground communities, provides an intricate structure of food and cover for animals, which in turn determines the structure of animal communities. The rich diversity of woody plants, as many as 1,000 species, in a high tropical rainforest with an elaborate layering of communities, provides an enormous variety of habitats for animals and opportunities for an endless variety of niches, the outcome of which is an incredible diversity among animal species. Another example of observable structure at the community level of systems is the physiognomy of sedentary communities of marine animals, including the corals, sea anemones, sponges, sea whips, and sea fans, so vividly displayed on TV in recent years. These structural arrangements of plant and animal communities recur in nature, with sufficient integrity as to be identifiable and serve as a systems level that is subject to scientific inquiry.

Because of its observability, vegetation (an integration of plant communities) has lent itself well to investigation, both in terms of structure and processes at the community level, so much so that the designation of major ecosystems is based on the earth's vegetation. The ecosystem concept seems to have grown out of studies of vegetation, in recognition of animal communities as integral parts of a higher-order system. The interrelatedness of plants is so well defined in some communities that one school of thought, in Europe, evolved a phytosociological approach, in which societies of plant populations are considered equivalent to a species, a viewpoint that exaggerates community integration as fixed linear interactions and interlocking braces. Free systems dynamics probably characterizes the formation of plant communities more than linear chain reactions, but not to the extent that each population of plant species is distributed entirely and completely independently of all other populations. It is impressive that plant communities do emerge, despite the variability of individual behavior of plants and populations of plants, and the process by which this occurs is comprehensible in terms of systems dynamics. An appreciation of the probablistic nature of the interactions is more readily developed through a systems approach, providing for statistical concepts and models of communities, through which to expand knowledge beyond that which is directly observable as vegetation in the field.

The process of vegetation change, or succession, on areas of abandoned farmland, forest clear-cuts followed by fire, or grassland released from heavy grazing by livestock, reflects the interactions of populations of different species of plants. Although the pattern of change is a continuum, "stages" can be recognized in the developing vegetation—such as forbs and annual grasses, perennial grasses, shrubs, and one or more types of forest. The underlying mechanisms of vegetation changes are not yet clear. It is thought that one community succeeds another, as the ecosystem is rendered less suitable for the existing plant communities and more suitable for the succeeding community. Relays of waves of plant disseminules from the surrounding ecosystems have been considered the primary source of new species composition during the process of succession. Recent studies in the northeastern United States cast doubt on the efficacy of this process as the dominant one in vegetation change, in view of the stability of shrub communities, and even herbaceous communities, following herbicidal removal of tree species. Most of the vegetation change in these 25-year studies seemed to emanate from plant species initially on the site at the time of abandonment from farming practices, but not to the total exclusion of the relay process. What is most remarkable is the relatively high predictability of the patterns of change, despite the highly probabilistic nature of the underlying mechanisms and the variability in the interactions between individual plants, which can best be interpreted on the basis of field continua and integral guidances of dynamic systems.

The process of succession involves developmental communities of animals and microorganisms as well as vegetation, and it also involves changes in the physical and chemical components of the area in which it occurs. It involves the total ecosystem, and although vegetation can be conceptually isolated for convenience in studying and managing this system, the interplay of plants, communities, and vegetation with other components of the ecosystem is essential to an adequate understanding of the process of vegetation change.

Populations; communities of populations of different organisms; vegetation as an integrated system of plant communities; biocommunities of populations systems of plants and animals; and human societies, can be viewed as major subsystems of an ecosystem in a geographical region of the earth, emerging from the field dynamics established by the collective behavior of the component organisms. All systems, from the organismic level downward, are also essential to the functioning of the total ecosystem, and it may be necessary to move to the molecular level to understand the limitations of ecosystem processes, such as energy flow, or the cycling of nitrogen, phosphorus, or other nutrients, but the phenomena that are unique at the ecosystem level seem to take form primarily out of its subsystems from the population upward.

An ecosystem is an open system with regard to the flow of energy that sustains it. Light energy, reaching the earth from the sun as photons, is converted to chemical energy in simple organic compounds, through the hydrogenation of carbon in the process of photosynthesis in green plants. About half of the potential energy, or gross productivity, is utilized in metabolic respiration by the food-producing plants, some is stored temporarily in the biomass of plants, and the net productivity flows into two types of food chains, one leading to herbivores and carnivores, and the other to organisms of decay. At each trophic level in the ecosystem's web of food chains some of the energy is stored in body tissues, temporarily, as biomass. Ultimately, all of the fixed energy is degraded and radiated into space as heat. A trophic structure emerges—from the interactions of the primary producers (almost exclusively chlorophyll-bearing plants), herbivorous primary consumers, carnivorous secondary and tertiary consumers, and decomposers such as fungi and bacteria—as food chains, food webs, pyramids of biomass or standing crop, and pyramids of numbers with a supporting base of numerically superior primary producers and a few top carnivores. The flow of energy through food webs, until all of the potential energy captured from the sun is degraded to heat, represents an ecosystem process that is unique for the system as a whole. The efficiency of the system is rather low, with only 0.1 to 0.3 percent of the solar radiation being fixed, and a transfer rate of 10 to 20 percent as the energy flows from one trophic level to another. In a developmental ecosystem, progressing toward a mature steady-state system, a portion of the net productivity is incorporated into the structure of the system as biomass, and into an elaboration of interactions among an increasing diversity of species components. In a mature ecosystem the net productivity approaches zero with no energy left over and no net annual storage. Such ecosystems reflect an evolutionary trend toward highly diversified, complex, homeostatically stable systems that make the most efficient use of the nonliving environmental matrix. This includes efficient mechanisms for recycling of the chemical elements that form the basis for living systems, including carbon, hydrogen, oxygen, sulfur, phosphorus, and several others, in respect to which an ecosystem is a closed system, subject to limitations when certain elements are in short supply. It is the complexity, arising from the diversity of organisms and their interplay, that determines the steady-state stability of mature ecosystems.

The total world ecosystem, prior to the advent of man, can be envisioned as a unified system with regional subsystems all tending toward increasing complexity and steady-state conditions. These nonhuman ecosystems represented the outcome of more than 3 billion years of evolutionary history, during which time upwards of 1 billion different species of organisms are estimated to have evolved, over 99 percent of which have become extinct. The ecosystems evolved as well as the species components. Terrestrial ecosystems are relatively recent evolutionary developments, dating back to about 400 million years ago, when living organisms began invading terrestrial environments from marine ecosystems. The evolution of arborescent vegetation enormously increased the opportunities for new niches, the proliferation of new species, and the development of highly complex ecosystems with self-regulating cybernetic controls, that provided relatively stable steady-state systems over long periods of time. About 2½ million years ago the human species was brought into being by these mature ecosystems. The resilience of these systems, exhibited in their capacity to recover from disturbances or perturbations imposed by the man-system over the past 5,000 years, is a measure of the integrity of ecosystems as highly organized dynamic systems. Man's technological capacity to destroy the integrity of ecosystems through irreversible changes is a relatively recent innovation.

The human mind, through which the man-system has been able to transcend many of the biological constraints of other forms of life, has added a new dimension to the world ecosystem. The term "noosphere" has been suggested as a new world envelope of the collective human mind, comparable in concept to the lithosphere (the nonliving solid earth), the atmosphere (the nonliving gaseous envelope), the hydrosphere (the nonliving aquatic aspect), and the biosphere (including all of the living organisms taken as a whole, exclusive of the nonliving environment). Together, these five spheres constitute the ecosphere, or total world ecosystem. The viewpoint of the earth in terms of its envelopes is useful in understanding the structure of the world ecosystem and major processes, such as the hydrologic cycle involved in biogeochemical recycling of materials in the closed system, and it helps to introduce the concept of the noosphere as a recent evolutionary development. It is the noosphere, functioning through modern technology, that now threatens the integrity of the world ecosystem. The current changes may be comparable in significance to the biological revolution of 2 billion years ago, when aerobic respiration evolved as a mechanism through which energy became available in quantities several orders of magnitude above that which was possible through primitive anaerobic fermentation processes, setting the stage for the evolution of higher, more complex living systems.

From an ecosystem viewpoint man has not transcended nature, and with all his unique humanistic attributes man can be viewed as a system in nature—as an integral part of the ecosystem that brought him into being. Population systems of man are so dominated by anthropocentric views, that the biological aspects of human behavior, the demographic behavior of his populations, ecosystem processes, and the evolution of the noosphere, are overshadowed by man's preoccupation with the arts, religion, political and social systems, and the economics of moving energy, materials, and consumer goods through the system. Man is capable of irreversibly altering the total world ecosystem by increasing the carbon dioxide content of the atmosphere, to a point where the greenhouse effect could warm the earth sufficiently to melt the polar ice caps; by interrupting vital processes such as photosynthesis, bacterial hydrogenation of sulphur, or nitrogen fixation by introducing new man-made chemicals, such as DDT and other highly toxic substances, into the ecosystem; by simplifying the species diversity and complexity of ecosystems, thereby destroying the resilience of systems to recover from disturbances; by reducing solar radiation by atmospheric pollution; and by increasing radioactivity to levels that are intolerable to living organisms.

The impact of man on the total ecosystem can be viewed as ecosystem processes at a new and higher-order level of systems organization, which can be conceptualized as the human ecosystem or the human-society-plus-total-environment level of organization. As a systems phenomenon the current biological revolution in the world ecosystem, brought on by the noosphere, can be viewed as being in a positive feedback phase, in which ever-higher levels of population encourage economic and technological growth at an ever-increasing expense to the diversity, complexity, and stability of the whole world ecosystem. If the real benefits from this process, in terms of the unfolding of the rich potentialities of the human species, are to be perpetuated and increased, conversion to a negative feedback system, through which a viable homeostatic (not static) stability can be achieved, is essential—otherwise the system will self-destruct. The present concerns with dehumanization in a technicized society, with the degradation of the quality of the human ecosystem, and with the quality of human life may be cybernetic signals that, hopefully, will trigger the conversion.

Viewing the human mind as an integral part of a new, higher-order ecosystem need not detract from the humanistic attributes of man, by reducing human society to a systems structure and behavior comparable to that of the lower levels of organized systems. Indeed, the uniqueness of the human ecosystem lies in the creativity of man, through which new integral configurations emerge. The human eco-system is a new and unique systems level of organization for the planet Earth. The current crisis lies in the threat of destroying the integrity of the world ecosystem as a life-support system through inadvertent, destructive modifications of the system. An understanding of ecosystem processes at the level of the total human ecosystem is needed, as a basis for bringing the system into functional harmony through technology, which is essential if the system is to be conducive to evolution of the noosphere toward the full potential of the human species. In today's world, the noosphere may be looked upon as the free systems dynamics of the human ecosystem, through which the system can adapt to the revolutionary changes brought on by the cultural evolution of man.

Sentences as Biological Systems

DAVID MCNEILL
University of Chicago

To those familiar with the development of transformational grammar in modern linguistics (Chomsky, 1965), there is a remarkable similarity between the way Paul Weiss describes the organization of biological phenomena and the way linguists describe the structure of sentences. My purpose in this short essay is simply to place these two domains—the linguistic and the biological—side by side and allow the parallel features to show themselves.

The most basic parallel lies in the *systemic* character of organization in both the biological and linguistic domains. When we perceive the meaning of a sentence in speech or print, the process shows many traits of a biological system. Why is this so? The domains, apparently, are entirely different; we are comparing the behavior of cells and their components to the behavior of sentences and their parts, and it seems fanciful to equate them. However, as Weiss argues, the basic units in every scientific field are conceptual abstractions; this is as true of cells as of sentences. The existence of a hidden similarity between two such abstractions is not impossible, no matter how far apart they may at first glance seem to be. In fact, as my title announces, sentences can be viewed as biological systems.

A justification for this claim can be reached in several ways. I will mention the three that are most revealing.

1. Regularities within sentences exist on a "macroscale," while on the "microscale" there is individual unpredictability. Thus, the individual words of a sentence can be

substituted at will within wide limits, without changing the structure of the sentence. This freedom exists with the so-called "content" words, the nouns, verbs, adjectives and adverbs, but not with the "function" words. Function words encode the structure of the sentence and hence belong to the constant macroscale, whereas content words encode the unpredictable microscale. Some examples:

(a) The teacher was firm but reasonable

(b) The weather was cloudy but warm

(c) The swarf was thrunkt but fetord

(d) But teacher the firm was reasonable

A constant pattern in (a)-(c) exists on the level of syntax, i.e., on the macroscale that encompasses the total sentence, but there is no pattern on the microscale where the choice of individual content words is made. In (d) the microscale of content words is as in (a), but the macroscale, as shown by the new arrangement of function words, is different. It is important to see the sense in which the choice of content words is unpredictable. It is hardly random from the speaker's point of view, since content words express his meaning. But this pattern of meaning does not come from the sentence. It comes from the situation and the speaker's intentions. From the point of view of the sentence structure it is not necessary even to know the meaning of the words; the Jabberwocky of (c) has the same pattern as (a) and (b). This pattern exists only on a macroscale and is in this respect like biological organization.

In another resemblance to biological organization, the structure of speech is hierarchical. As one plunges into the microscale, indeterminacy increases, but at the same time, one encounters fresh macroscales further down in a hierarchy of structure. Within every word, which itself is an adventitious member of a sentence pattern, is a systematic phonological pattern. In turn, the phonological pattern introduces a fresh microscale of indeterminate phonetic variations that possess no linguistic significance (but are macroscopically related to still deeper levels, e.g., the neural activation of the speech musculature). This hierarchy in speech corresponds to the distinction between a bodily organ and a cell. There is patterning on both levels, but the upper level cannot be reduced to the lower one.

A classic example of phonological patterning is the restriction of the first member of an English consonant cluster to /s/ when the cluster initiates a word (Halle, 1964). The first three words below occur in English but the last three do not and never could, without a radical change of the English sound pattern:

> smell
> scratch
> start
> *mpell
> *kshun
> *ntart

This restriction has nothing to do with the difficulty of pronouncing or hearing clusters not beginning with /s/; non-/s/ clusters exist initially in other languages and in non-initial places in English. The forbidden clusters above all appear medially or finally in *compel, action* (the "c" of which phonetically /k/), and *plant*. The requirement that /s/ occur first is a restriction on the phonological macroscale, not the phonetic microscale.[1]

On the phonetic microscale are innumerable variations in the acoustic signals for speech and the muscular events that produce them. The most dramatic evidence of hierarchical

1. There are, of course, many words starting with consonants other than /s/ when the second phoneme is /l/ or /r/: *cling, crash, glimpse, truck*, etc. According to Halle (1964), however, /l/ and /r/ are not themselves true consonants, and hence are not restricted to clusters with /s/, but are a fusion of consonant and vowel properties.

organization at this level is the complete *absence* of an effect
on the intelligibility of speech by changing the speaker
(from male to female or adult to child) or the mode of
speaking (from quiet conversation to shout). The phonetic
details move up and down the frequency and amplitude
scales in a fashion that can only be called cavalier, yet there
is no effect on the perception of phonological structure.
Studies of these switches have been made and find that
listeners rapidly adjust to the new level (Ladefoged, 1967).
It is accomplished within a few words, i.e., within a few
seconds of speech. Relating the first bit of speech to the
phonological pattern moves the entire phonetic scale up or
down, which shows clearly the dominance of the pattern.

2. Returning to the level of syntax, we can see the systemic organization of language in another aspect of sentence
structure. Ambiguity is often decried, but it is to be expected
if sentences are systems. In systems of all kinds, not only
is the structure of the whole independent in large measure
of the parts, but understanding the interrelation of the parts
requires knowing the state of the whole, as Weiss points
out. In the case of sentences ambiguity results when the
same parts are coordinated by different wholes. Ambiguities
are therefore especially clear examples of the dominance of
wholes over parts in sentence organization. To give one
simple instance,

"they are flying planes"

has two senses, each of which is correlated with a different
organization of the words. In the sense where *they* refers
to "pilots" the words *are* and *flying* coalesce into a constituent, whereas in the sense where *they* refers to "planes" *flying* and *planes* coalesce. The pronoun *they* does not coalesce
with any word, but it alone among the words of the sentence
changes meaning, showing clearly that these changes take
place across the whole sentence. Depending on the state of
the whole (the meaning of the sentence) the parts are af-

fected in different ways. Using parentheses to indicate constituents, the two senses of *they are flying* are correlated with the following patterns:

> (they) (are flying) (planes)　　they = pilots
> (they) (are) (flying planes)　　they = planes

In actual speech such ambiguities usually pass unnoticed. The reason is simply that, in a natural situation, the context makes immediately clear the sense in which sentences are to be understood, leaving only one organization of the parts and so no ambiguity to be noticed. If *they are flying planes* was the answer to a question about two people, then following the systemic principle of the whole determining the parts, there would be no basis for noticing that *they* could also mean "planes." Many attempts to perform an automatic sentence analysis with computers have failed because they have overlooked this systemic character of language. The computer has been made to work on the reverse assumption that the whole can be reduced to the parts and is soon lost in a forest of ambiguities, trying inductively to reach the overall organization of the sentence from the bottom up. For a spectacular illustration of the consequences of overlooking the systemic aspects of language, see Kuno and Oettinger (1963), whose program was able to find up to four or five distinct interpretations of such English sentences as "People who apply for marriage licenses wearing shorts or pedal pushers will be denied licenses."

3. Weiss suggests that, as a test of a biological system, a unit should be able to regain equilibrium after interference with one of its parts. Cells come and go but unless the going outruns the coming on a large scale, the organ of which the cells are a part remains stable. Daily experience provides many examples of sentences that pass this test. Sentence structure easily survives the mispronunciation of words, hesitations, false starts and changes in direction, and innumerable other distortions that develop in speaking. The

sentence rises smoothly behind this jagged front. To illustrate how, I have reproduced below a verbatim transcript of a few moments from a psychiatric interview (Pittenger, Hockett, and Danehy, 1960). The reader can verify for himself, by reading out loud, that interruptions in the flow of speech do not prevent the build-up of sentence structure. (The spaces show pauses, with the length of the space corresponding to the length of the pause.) Notice how extraneous noises, such as a throat being cleared or sighing, are automatically ejected from the process of understanding what is being said. False starts, such as "But I w-I need a rest," literally do not fit the structure of English, but they are instantly disregarded once their status as false starts is known. The perception of sentence structure is not bothered by what is, according to any measure, a radical distortion of the parts of sentences.

"Well (clears throat)   (sigh)   for instance   I
    I'm supposed to do some relief   duty   (sigh)
two weeks   this   month uhh next month September
    (sigh)   And he makes it   so miserable for me
that   I'm in a constant stew   (sigh) And he says that
my place is home with the children.   I agree   But I
w-I need a rest.   I need to get away from them. I need to
be   with   well with people. (sigh) I can't stay
closeted up in the house all the time" (Pittenger, et al., pp. 49a-77a).

In addition to such natural examples, there is a long history of psychological experimentation that consists essentially of the successful application of Weiss's test to the perception of sentences. Miller, Heise, and Lichten (1951), for example, used a white noise to mask speech and measured the intelligibility of words. They did this under two conditions, once when the words were heard separately, one by one, and another time when the same words were heard in the context of sentences. Intelligibility was always greater when the words were part of a sentence. A white noise randomly distorts the speech signal; at low signal-to-noise ratios the degree of randomness is quite large. That speech can be perceived at all under these conditions of high entropy is vivid proof that, in the perception of speech, as in a biological system, there is a channelling of effects to conserve the integrated state of the whole. How this occurs in the perception of speech is no less puzzling than how it occurs in living systems, but the logical nature of the problem is the same in the two cases. That words are better perceived in the context of a sentence than in isolation means that the overall sentence pattern is less easily disrupted than the separate words. The resistance of a linguistic unit to disruption by a random noise therefore depends on its position in the overall linguistic hierarchy. Larger units, higher in the hierarchy, are more difficult to topple. Such a layering of protection, being greater for higher units, is of obvious practical value in a world filled with nonspeech sounds, and rests directly on the systemic character of language.

*   *   *

What gives sentence structure a systemic character? The answer comes from the form taken by sentences as this is shown in a transformational grammar. A simple diagram displays the main relationships:[2]

The abstract and superficial structure, together with the transformations that relate them, describe the entire pattern

2. There is an irrelevant but confusing conflict of terminology between transformational grammar and Weiss's Essay on Hierarchical Systems, in that what is "higher" in a Weiss hierarchy is the "deep" or "underlying" structure of sentences. To avoid confusion I will refer to "abstract structure" rather than to "deep structure."

of a sentence. The superficial structure can be sensed—heard or seen—while the abstract structure must be apprehended and cannot be sensed. Some examples will make these points clear:

(a) They are drinking wine   (gerund)
(b) They are drinking companions   (adjective nominal)
(c) They are drinking glasses   (predicate nominal)

At a most superficial level sentences (a)-(c) are much alike. Each includes *they, are,* and *drinking;* the sentences differ only in the final noun. However, by going into the sentences a short distance, we immediately discover a difference in structure between (a) on the one hand and (b)-(c) on the other. In (a) *drinking is* coalesced with *are,* while in the two nominals it is coalesced with the following nouns. This abstract difference can be made concrete. If the definite article *the* is inserted into (a) it must go after *drinking,* whereas in (b) and (c) it must go before it.

If we push still further we discover a difference also between sentences (b) and (c). Consider how they can be paraphrased:

Sentence	*Paraphrase*
(b) They are drinking companions	They are companions who drink
(c) They are drinking glasses	They are glasses to use for drinking

The form of the paraphrase cannot be exchanged between (b) and (c) without losing the meaning of the original. However, there is nothing in the superficial structure of either (b) or (c) that indicates this, by now, completely abstract difference. It is a difference that can be apprehended but not sensed.

The successive differences traced with these examples occur at increasingly abstract levels, i.e., at levels less and less well reflected in the overt form of the sentence. Between (a), (b), and (c) separately there is a highly superficial difference in the final noun. Between (a) and (b)-(c) there is a more abstract difference in where *the* can be, but need not be, inserted. And between (b) and (c) there is a difference that can be made overt only through a radical change of structure (paraphrase). Such levels of abstraction correspond to the levels of the hierarchy of sentence structure which I discussed before and linked with the concept of a biological system. The basis for this linkage is exactly that sentences include a hierarchy of abstraction. The most constant and least vulnerable aspect of sentences is the completely abstract part that is never reflected at the surface. The ultimate sentence pattern is therefore a *mental* pattern.

We can find in this fact an explanation of why sentences show the properties of biological systems. The most abstract levels of sentence structure cannot be sensed. They must be apprehended. Rejecting a mind-body dualism in which mental events can exist without correlated brain events, this linguistic fact commits us to the idea that sentences do not exist without the correlated activity of a literal biological system. The process of understanding or producing speech depends in this view on the establishment of an actual ongoing system within the brain. Since different sentences presumably depend on different systems, these biolinguistic systems are unusual in being short-lived, but in other respects behave like all biological systems. Producing and perceiving speech, for example, can be viewed as the very rapid ontogenesis of a system.

REFERENCES

Chomsky, N. *Aspects of the theory of syntax*. Cambridge, Mass.: MIT Press, 1965.

Halle, M. Phonology in a generative grammar. In J. A. Fodor and J. J. Katz (Eds.). *The structure of language: readings in the philosophy of language*. Englewood Cliffs, N.J.: Prentice-Hall, 1964. Pp. 334-352.

Kuno, S. and Oettinger, A. Syntactic structure and ambiguity of English. In J. D. Tupac (Ed.). *Proceedings of the fall joint computer conference*. Baltimore: Spartan Books, 1967. Pp. 397-418.

Ladfoged, P. *Three areas of experimental phonetics*. London: Oxford Univ. Press, 1967.

Miller, G. A., Heise, G. A., and Lichten, W. The intelligibility of speech as a function of the context of the test materials. *Journal of experimental psychology*, 1951, *41*, 329-335.

Pittenger, R. E., Hockett, C. F. and Danehy, J. J. *The first five minutes*. Ithaca, N.Y.: Paul Martineau, 1960.

Social Systems

JAMES S. COLEMAN
Johns Hopkins University

Once when I was sitting on the edge of a cliff, a bundle of gnats hovered in front of me, and offered a strange sight. Each gnat was flying at high speed, yet the bundle was motionless. Each gnat sped in an ellipse, spanning the diameter of the bundle, and by his frenetic flight, maintaining the bundle motionless. Suddenly, the bundle itself darted —and then hovered again. It expanded and its boundaries became diffuse; then it contracted into a tight, hard knot and darted again—all the while composed of nothing other than gnats flying their endless ellipses. It finally moved off and disappeared. Perhaps also it dissipated and ceased to exist, each gnat going his own way.

Such a phenomenon offers enormous intellectual problems: how is each gnat's flight guided, when its direction bears almost no relation to the direction of the bundle? How does he maintain the path of his endless ellipse? And how does he come to change it, when the bundle moves? What is the structure of control, and what are the signals by which control is transmitted?

But the problems are not only substantive; they are also problems of what conceptual framework is best used to describe systematically what goes on. When are the gnats and their actions the best units for describing behavior, when is the bundle the best unit, and when is still a third more ingenious conceptual scheme necessary?

As with this bundle of gnats, there are serious conceptual problems in studying the organized behavior of men. Over time, new modes of social organization have been invented, and following in the invention's wake have been sociologists desperately trying to comprehend and name the new mode of organization, and describe how it functions.

THE COMMONSENSE FRAME

There is a perfectly good commonsense way of describing social behavior. Individuals are the basic units, they combine into groups to form larger units, and those groups combine into still larger units,—being each a "group of groups." Action is then described either as action of an *individual*, or of a *group*, which may be at any level of aggregation. Each action has a subject and an object of action, and the subject may be an individual or a group, as can the object also. But if there are not to be serious conceptual problems, then certain ground rules must be established. For example, if an individual takes an action toward a *group* of individuals, or even toward an individual in a group different from his own, then is he acting as an *individual* or as a *group member*, thus binding or committing his group to the action?

Such questions are more than exercises about the rules of a conceptual system; they are questions about the actual functioning of social systems. In many tribal societies, an individual is wholly encompassed by his single group membership, and can take no actions as an individual outside that group. If he does so, then his action is a group action, which is reacted to by the other group, and for which his group—not he alone—is held responsible. Among Appalachian clans, for example, violence within the clan was punished by the aggrieved party or by the authority system of the clan, meting out punishment to the individual for his action. When violence occurred between clans, however, the offending party was taken to be the clan itself, and the clan itself is punished by an action of the aggrieved clan.

Such relations are characteristic of a particular type of

social organization, for which the commonsense mode of description is appropriate. This type of social organization, which may be described as "whole-person organization," is characteristic of the middle ages in western society, of most tribally-based social systems, and in fact, in general of social systems in which groupings are based on blood lines. In these systems, the whole person is within a group, and he has no social existence outside that group. (This makes ostracism a particularly interesting test. There are recorded cases in which individuals, ostracized from a tribe, have simply died for psychological reasons, unable to exist outside it.) The individual is encapsulated by the group, and any relation outide it is legitimate only if it is carried out through normal group-relation channels.

This principle can exist quite well for hierarchically-organized systems, in which an individual is a member of successively more inclusive groups. For example, the following description indicates how such a system works in a particular kind of action:

> The political functioning of the lineage system . . . can be illustrated from what happens when a member of one lineage kills a member of another in the clan diagrammatically represented below. It is to be remembered that the letters do not represent historic individuals only, but larger or smaller groups of living persons tracing descent from those individuals:
>
> Here the letters represent lineages of different orders, all claiming descent from A, and thence, in the male line, through B, C, D, E, and so on. If a member of lineage H kills a member of lineage I, then all members of H and all members of I are potentially at enmity with one another. Others are not necessarily involved. But if a member of H or I kills a member of J or K all H and I (now regarding themselves as member of D) may be engaged in hostilities with all J and K (now

united as E). So also all B lineage will tend to unite
against all C lineage if a man from one kills a man from
the other; and finally the whole of A will be united—
in theory at least—against outsiders who have injured
any one of their members.

Leinhardt (1964, p. 72-73)

In its more developed and extensive forms, this mode of
social organization takes on added complexity, introduced
by distinguishing different actions. For example, among
the Beduin nomads in the Sudan a man is a member of one
group (an *Ahl*) with respect to water rights and avenging
of homicides, and another smaller and wholly included
group (a *biyut*) with respect to camel herd rights. For
transgressions relating to water rights or for homicides,
his *ahl* is held responsible; for transgressions relating to
camel herds, his *biyut* is held responsible. (See Peters, 1959,
Muhsam, 1966). It is not wholly clear how such systems
are most profitably conceptualized, nor is it fully clear what
happens when actions such as homicides occur between
members of the same *ahl* (el Hakeem, 1969). These systems
are distinct, however, from the simpler systems in which
the individual is a member only of the first-level group, and
the second-level group had as members the first-level groups,
with a duplication of rights and responsibilities at each
level.

The development of society in the western world since
the middle ages has, however, led to greater complexity of
social organization, requiring greater complexity of conceptual structure. For note that such social organization as
described above cannot tolerate an individual's simultaneous
membership in groups which are only partly overlapping.
If an individual who is wholly incorporated in groups A
and B offends a person who is wholly a member of group
B only, then by one principle, group B would necessarily
take vengeance upon group A, while by the other it would

be a dispute internal to group B. The means of resolving this ambiguity is for the individual's membership in one group to be broken.

SOCIAL ORGANIZATION COMPOSED OF POSITIONS OR RULES

A more complex social system has emerged in the past few centuries in the western world, fundamentally different from the whole-person organization of society. In this organization, persons are not the elements of organization at all; rather, positions are. The position has certain attributes, that is actions which its occupant should carry out and actions he can expect from persons in other roles. But the individual is merely the tenant of the role; the organization exists independently of him, just as an apartment building exists independently of its tenants. This distinction between the whole person and the role as the unit of which the organization is composed was a remarkable conceptual invention, for it freed the individual from confinement by the group, and it allowed the creation of groups or organizations which were single-purposed, cutting away most of the needs and interests of individuals.

The most extreme example of such organization is the bureaucracy, which in pure form is merely a purposive organization consisting of roles or positions. The individual occupants of the roles may lead it to function well or poorly; but the organization is defined wholly independently of its occupants.

This mode of social organization has made it possible for individuals to increase their range and flexibility of activity enormously. For now they are no longer a *member* of an organization or group, captive of it, but may eclectically participate in a number of organizations. Indeed, one sociologist, George Simmel, has argued that the idea of individuality in its present-day sense and intellectuality derived from the new form of social organization. In this new form, the individual was the unique intersection of a number of circles representing groups or organizations. In the previous form, he was merely surrounded, with others like himself, by a set of concentric circles.

There is as well a somewhat surprising further consequence to this reconstruction of social organization. Individuals constitute one set of elements, each a purposive acting entity, each occupying positions or roles. The organization of roles, that is, the purposive social organization, is another type of element in society, with many of the same properties as actors that the individual has. Thus slowly and with difficulty, the idea of a new kind of actor in society emerged, the corporation. The idea of the corporation—not corporation in the narrow sense, but any corporate body organized for a purpose and structurally composed of roles or positions in fixed relation—grew slowly in the middle ages, taking its roots from the dual sources of Roman law and Germanic law (von Gierke, 1961). Society is thus transformed from a system consisting of individuals-in-relation to one consisting of individuals-and-corporations in relation. It is much as if a lake is transformed from one with only trout to one with trout and bass. But it is more complicated than this, because the corporations and individuals are not only in interaction as purposive actors (as when a *man* makes a purchase from a *store*), but are also in symbolic relation (as when a *man* works as a clerk in a *store*). Furthermore, the corporations as elements of a social system must necessarily be conceived differently from individuals. They are not tangible; they have no fixed life cycle; they have no fixed central nervous system which provides central authority. Their problems both in practice and theory lie principally in two areas: since they are not tangible, they require special regulation as an *object* of action, e.g., where does liability lie, and how can that liability be fixed on an intangible entity, and as a *subject* of action, e.g., how can they be so organized and directed that they will take purposive action to reach their goals? These problems of liability and organizational decision-making are two important ones both in legal practice and in social theory. Equally important, the modus vivendi between these intangible corporate bodies as social actors and concrete individual persons as social actors has been only poorly developed in practice and in theory. The human actors have little power relative to the corporate actors, and few ways have been found of redressing the power imbalance. The human actors are also less responsible than the corporate actors, especially in their actions toward corporate actors as distinct from other persons. In short, the theory and practice of the flexible dualistic social structure of which western society currently consists is deficient in numerous ways. Until the power imbalance is redressed, until corporate bodies can take action as resolutely as can persons, and until persons' actions toward corporations can be made more humane, the structure and its theoretical and legal underpinnings must remain defective.

The theoretical problems of these corporate bodies can be illustrated by those attending just one of the three problems described above: the problems of taking action as a corporate body. These problems derive from the fact that each individual who occupies a position in the corporate body is acting from the point of view of the interests of the occupant of his position; yet the corporate body's action, made up of the system of actions of the individuals who occupy positions in it, must be in *its* interest. In a very loosely-structured corporate body, there is the "free-rider" problem (Olson, 1965). This is exemplified by support for a volunteer fire department in a community. The fire department protects the entire community from fire; but if it is supported by contributions, then it is to each individual's benefit not to contribute. For if his neighbors contribute, then the fire equipment will be purchased and his home will be protected, whether he contributes or not. And if his neighbors do not contribute, then his contribution alone is not sufficient to buy the equipment, and he therefore is unprotected, whether or not he contributes.

The general phenomenon arises whenever the *consequences* of an action fall on a number of individuals, and cannot be separated (i.e., if a fire department is available to my neighbors, it is available to me). Then, unless there is a way to insure that all individuals on whom the consequences fall contribute to the action, none will contribute. The problem appears quite widely, not only for public goods, like fire departments, but also for the loss of public goods, such as pollution of the air in a city. Here the necessary action to which individuals must contribute is refraining from polluting. Since all experience the consequences of each's polluting actions, and he is very little affected by his own, then it is to no individual's interest to refrain from polluting, though it is to the interest of all for all to refrain from polluting.

This problem of corporate action in which each escapes contribution and all suffer is created by the absence of the appropriate system of sanctions—the absence of organization. If the corporate body is appropriately organized, it can impose sanctions (punishment for failure to pay taxes or for breaking the law) which insure that the individual will not experience the common benefit at a cost to others. But the problem lies in the fact that the set of actions changes, with the system of sanctions always lagging behind. (E.g., people experience air pollution only when the density of people in a given place increases beyond a certain point.) Thus the organization must continually change to remain able to carry out its collective actions effectively.

A related problem of corporate action is the problem of synthesizing individual preferences into a collective action, when there is lack of consensus. There may be no collective action that can be consistently arrived at by application of a decision rule. For example, with three alternatives, A, B, and C, three voters, X, Y, and Z, and a majority rule, suppose we have the following rank orders (with 1 representing first preference):

Rank	X	Y	Z
1	A	B	C
2	B	C	A
3	C	A	B

If the alternatives A and B are first pitted against one another, A wins by the vote of X and Z. But if A and C are the first pair, C wins by vote of Y and Z, and in the contest between C and B, B wins by vote of X and Y. Thus the same set of individual preferences lead inconsistently to different collective actions, depending on the order of voting.

This peculiarity of corporate action, in which consistent individual preferences lead to inconsistent corporate actions, is a major problem in the theory of collective action. It is not possible, in fact, to devise decision rules that will be free of such inconsistencies, unless the decision rule is dictatorial direction by a single individual in a position of absolute authority (Arrow, 1951). This is, upon reflection, probably inevitable: the only way to insure that a corporate body will act wholly like a rational individual actor in having a consistent set of preferences for action is for it to act under the direction of an individual. It is undoubtedly this that leads nations to use far more centralized decision rules when the nation is at war or in internal distress and cannot afford irresolute action.

These two problems of corporate action, the free rider problem and the problem of inconsistent corporate actions derived from consistent individual preferences, show some of the special theoretical problems created by the existence of corporate actors as elements of a social system, the same social systems of which individual actors who occupy positions in these corporate actors are also elements.

SOCIAL INVENTIONS

The social structures described above can be thought of as social inventions—inventions of new structures which have fewer strains than do old ones. The rapid transition of western society from rural to urban society can in part be seen as the escape from strains of the single-structure form of organization based on whole persons, of which rural life is largely composed, to the dualistic structure of individuals and corporate bodies found largely in urban life. But it is clear also that urban life, and more generally the dualistic form of social organization, itself shows numerous strains. Thus the question arises, what new concepts of social organization will emerge, allowing even greater flexibility? Only conjectures are possible at this point in time. However, one interesting pattern seems to be a time mixture of the whole-person basis of organization and the dualistic form of organization with corporate bodies as a second set of elements. The growth of "encounter groups," group therapy and other forms of short-term whole-person involvement suggests such a time mixture as a possibility. Many people may come to alternate between these two patterns on a daily or weekly basis, or with a longer periodicity. It is possible to see the family in modern industrial society as the whole-person form of organization with most individuals alternating daily between participation in that entity and participating in corporate bodies of which they are merely role occupants. However, families are a residue of the earlier forms of whole-person involvement, which require continuity over time. The distinctive character of these newly-developing whole-person entities is that they are impermanent, and imply only a temporary commitment.

These conjectures about possible new forms of social organization indicate just how linked together are our forms of social organization and our ways of thinking about systems. Our inability to create new forms of social organization perhaps more suited to present technology lies largely in our inability to *conceive* of these forms. For once conceived, they come to be tried, if past history is an indicator, and end by becoming social inventions which then stand to be described by social theory.

In all this, the similarity of these problems to those described by Weiss in conceptualizing biological systems is striking. The fundamental question of what is the subject of action, i.e., what is the appropriate unit of analysis, is the same in both fields, as are many of the other conceptual problems. It may not be too much to hope that solution of some of these problems in one type of system may lead to their solution in others.

REFERENCES

Arrow, Kenneth. *Social Choice and Individual Values* (New York: John Wiley), 1951.

el Hakeem, Sherif M. "Segmentary Lineage Theory and Beduin Politics," mimeographed, John Hopkins University, Baltimore, Md., 1969.

Lienhardt, G. *Social Anthropology* (London: Oxford University Press), 1964.

Muhsam, H. V. *Beduin of the Negev* (Jerusalem Academic Press), 1966.

Olson, Mancur. *The Logic of Collective Action* (Cambridge: Harvard University Press), 1965.

Peters, Emrys L. "The Proliferation of Segments in the Lineage of the Beduin of Cyrenaica, JRAI, LXXXIX, 29-53, 1959.

von Gierke, Otto. "The Idea of Corporation," in *Theories of Society*, T. Parsons, E. Shils, K. Naegele, J. Pitts (eds.) (New York: The Free Press of Glencoe), 1961.

Behavior of Social Systems

JAY W. FORRESTER*
*Sloan School of Management, Massachusetts Institute
of Technology*

System dynamics has demonstrated how companies and
how urban systems behave in ways that run against most
of what man would do to correct their ills. Now the same
obtuse behavior can be assigned to the largest social issues
which confront the nation and the world.

This paper addresses several issues of broad concern in
the United States: population trends; the quality of urban
life; national policy for urban growth; and the unexpected,
ineffective, or detrimental results often generated by government programs in these areas.

The nation exhibits a growing sense of futility as it repeatedly attacks deficiencies in our social system while the
symptoms continue to worsen. Legislation is debated and
passed with great promise and hope. But many programs
prove to be ineffective. Results often seem unrelated to
those expected when the programs were planned. At times
programs cause exactly the reverse of desired results.

It is now possible to explain how such contrary results
can happen. There are fundamental reasons why people mis-
judge the behavior of social systems. There are orderly
processes at work in the creation of human judgment and

* This paper is copyright 1970 by J. W. Forrester. It is based on
testimony for the Subcommittee on Urban Growth of the Committee
on Banking and Currency, U.S. House of Representatives, on October
7, 1970, and was previously published in *Technology Review* Vol. 73,
No. 3, January 1971 by the Alumni Association of the Massachusetts
Institute of Technology.

intuition that frequently lead people to wrong decisions when faced with complex and highly interacting systems. Until we come to a much better understanding of social systems, we should expect that attempts to develop corrective programs will continue to disappoint us.

The purpose of this paper is to leave with its readers a sense of caution about continuing to depend on the same past approaches that have led to our present feeling of frustration and to suggest an approach which can eventually lead to a better understanding of our social systems and thereby to more effective policies for guiding the future.

A NEW APPROACH TO SOCIAL SYSTEMS

It is my basic theme that the human mind is not adapted to interpreting how social systems behave. Our social systems belong to the class called multi-loop nonlinear feedback systems. In the long history of evolution it has not been necessary for man to understand these systems until very recent historical times. Evolutionary processes have not given us the mental skill needed to properly interpret the dynamic behavior of the systems of which we have now become a part.

In addition, the social sciences have fallen into some mistaken "scientific" practices which compound man's natural shortcomings. Computers are often being used for what the computer does poorly and the human mind does well. At the same time the human mind is being used for what the human mind does poorly and the computer does well. Even worse, impossible tasks are attempted while achievable and important goals are ignored.

Until recently there has been no way to estimate the behavior of social systems except by comtemplation, discussion, argument and guesswork. To point a way out of our present dilemma about social systems, I will sketch an approach that combines the strength of the human mind and the strength of today's computers. The approach is an outgrowth of developments over the last forty years, in which much of the research has been at the Massachusetts Institute of Technology. The concepts of feedback system behavior apply sweepingly from physical systems through social systems. The ideas were first developed and applied to engineering systems. They have now reached practical usefulness in major aspects of our social systems.

I am speaking of what has come to be called "industrial dynamics." The name is a misnomer because the methods apply to complex systems regardless of the field in which they are located. A more appropriate name would be "system dynamics." In our own work, applications have been made to corporate policy, to the dynamics of diabetes as a medical system, to the growth and stagnation of an urban area, and most recently to world dynamics representing the interactions of population, pollution, industrialization, natural resources, and food. System dynamics, as an extension of the earlier design of physical systems, has been under development at M.I.T. since 1956. The approach is easy to understand but difficult to practice. Few people have a high level of skill; but preliminary work is developing all over the world. Some European countries and especially Japan have begun centers of education and research.

COMPUTER MODELS OF SOCIAL SYSTEMS

People would never attempt to send a space ship to the moon without first testing the equipment by constructing prototype models and by computer simulation of the anticipated space trajectories. No company would put a new kind of household appliance or electronic computer into production without first making laboratory tests. Such models and laboratory tests do not guarantee against failure, but they do identify many weaknesses which can then be corrected before they cause full-scale disasters.

Our social systems are far more complex and harder to understand than our technological systems. Why, then, do we not use the same approach of making models of social systems and conducting laboratory experiments on those models before we try new laws and government programs in real life? The answer is often stated that our knowledge of social systems is insufficient for constructing useful models. But what justification can there be for the apparent assumption that we do not know enough to construct models but believe we do know enough to directly design new social systems by passing laws and starting new social programs? I am suggesting that we now do know enough to make useful models of social systems. Conversely, we do not know enough to design the most effective systems directly without first going through a model-building experimental phase. But I am confident, and substantial supporting evidence is beginning to accumulate, that the proper use of models of social systems can lead to far better systems, and to laws and programs that are far more effective than those created in the past.

It is now possible to construct in the laboratory realistic models of social systems. Such models are simplifications of the actual social system but can be far more comprehensive than the mental models that we otherwise use as the basis for debating governmental action.

Before going further, I should emphasize that there is nothing new in the use of models to represent social systems. Each of us uses models constantly. Every person in his private life and in his business life instinctively uses models for decision making. The mental image of the world around you which you carry in your head is a model. One does not have a city or a government or a country in his head. He has only selected concepts and relationships which he uses to represent the real system. A mental image is a model. All of our decisions are taken on the basis of models. All of our laws are passed on the basis of models. All executive actions are taken on the basis of models. The question is not to use or ignore models. The question is only a choice among alternative models.

The mental model is fuzzy. It is incomplete. It is imprecisely stated. Furthermore, within one individual, a mental model changes with time and even during the flow of a single conversation. The human mind assembles a few relationships to fit the context of a discussion. As the subject shifts so does the model. When only a single topic is being discussed, each participant in a conversation employs a different mental model to interpret the subject. Fundamental assumptions differ but are never brought into the open. Goals are different and are left unstated. It is little wonder that compromise takes so long. And it is not surprising that consensus leads to laws and programs that fail in their objectives or produce new difficulties greater than those that have been relieved.

For these reasons we stress the importance of being explicit about assumptions and interrelating them in a computer model. Any concept or assumption that can be clearly described in words can be incorporated in a computer model. When done, the ideas become clear. Assumptions are exposed so they may be discussed and debated.

But the most important difference between the properly conceived computer model and the mental model is in the ability to determine the dynamic consequences when the assumptions within the model interact with one another. The human mind is not adapted to sensing correctly the consequences of a mental model. The mental model may be correct in structure and assumptions but, even so, the human mind—either individually or as a group consensus—is most apt to draw the wrong conclusions. There is no doubt about the digital computer routinely and accurately tracing through the sequences of actions that result from following the statements of behavior for individual points in the model system. This inability of the human mind to use its own mental models is clearly shown when a computer model is constructed to reproduce the assumptions held by a single person. In other words, the model is refined until it is fully agreeable in all its assumptions to the perceptions and ideas of a particular person. Then, it usually happens that the system that has been described does not act the way the person anticipated. Usually there is an internal contradiction in mental models between the assumed structure and the assumed future consequences. Ordinarily the assumptions about the structure and internal motivations are more nearly correct than are the assumptions about the implied behavior.

The kind of computer models that I am discussing are strikingly similar to mental models. They are derived from the same sources. They may be discussed in the same terms. But computer models differ from mental models in important ways. The computer models are stated explicitly. The "mathematical" notation that is used for describing the model is unambiguous. It is a language that is clearer, simpler and more precise than such spoken languages as English or French. Its advantage is in the clarity of meaning and the simplicity of the language syntax. The language of a computer model can be understood by almost anyone, regardless of educational background. Furthermore, any concept and relationship that can be clearly stated in ordinary language can be translated into computer model language.

There are many approaches to computer models. Some are naive. Some are conceptually and structurally inconsistent with the nature of actual systems. Some are based on methodologies for obtaining input data that commit the models to omitting major concepts and relationships in the psychological and human reaction areas that we all know to be crucial. With so much activity in computer models and with the same terminology having different meanings in the different approaches, the situation must be confusing to the casual observer. The key to success is not in having a computer; the important thing is how the computer is used. With respect to models, the key is not to computerize a model, but instead to have a model structure and relationships which properly represent the system that is being considered.

I am speaking here of a kind of computer model that is very different from the models that are now most common in the social sciences. Such a computer model is not derived statistically from time-series data. Instead, the kind of computer model I am discussing is a statement of system structure. It contains the assumptions being made about the system. The model is only as good as the expertise which lies behind its formulation. Great and correct theories in physics or in economics are few and far between. A great computer model is distinguished from a poor one by the degree to which it captures more of the essence of the social system that it presumes to represent. Many mathematical models are limited because they are formulated by techniques and according to a conceptual structure that will not accept the multiple-feedback-loop and nonlinear nature of real systems. Other models are defective because of lack of knowledge or deficiencies of perception on the part of the persons who have formulated them.

But a recently developed kind of computer modeling is now beginning to show the characteristics of behavior of actual systems. These models explain why we are having the present difficulties with our actual social systems and furthermore explain why so many efforts to improve social systems have failed. In spite of their shortcomings, models can now be constructed that are far superior to the intuitive models in our heads on which we are now basing national social programs.

This approach to the dynamics of social systems differs in two important ways from common practice in social sciences and government. There seems to be a common attitude that the major difficulty is shortage of information and data.

Once data is collected, people then feel confident in interpreting the implications. I differ on both of these attitudes. The problem is not shortage of data but rather our inability to perceive the consequences of the information we already possess. The system dynamics approach starts with the concepts and information on which people are already acting. Generally these are sufficient. The available perceptions are then assembled in a computer model which can show the consequences of the well-known and properly perceived parts of the system. Generally, the consequences are unexpected.

COUNTERINTUITIVE NATURE OF SOCIAL SYSTEMS

Our first insights into complex social systems came from our corporate work. Time after time we have gone into a corporation which is having severe and well-known difficulties. The difficulties can be major and obvious such as a falling market share, low profitability, or instability of employment. Such difficulties are known throughout the company and by anyone outside who reads the management press. One can enter such a company and discuss with people in key decision points what they are doing to solve the problem. Generally speaking we find that people perceive correctly their immediate environment. They know what they are trying to accomplish. They know the crises which will force certain actions. They are sensitive to the power structure of the organization, to traditions, and to their own personal goals and welfare. In general, when circumstances are conducive to frank disclosure, people can state what they are doing and can give rational reasons for their actions. In a troubled company, people are usually trying in good conscience and to the best of their abilities to solve the major difficulties. Policies are being followed at the various points in the organization on the presumption that they will alleviate the difficulties. One can combine these policies into a computer model to show the consequences of how the policies interact with one another. In many instances it then emerges that the known policies describe a system which actually causes the troubles. In other words, the known and intended practices of the organization are fully sufficient to create the difficulty, regardless of what happens outside the company or in the marketplace. In fact, a downward spiral develops in which the presumed solution makes the difficulty worse and thereby causes redoubling of the presumed solution so that matters become still worse.

The same downward spiral frequently develops in government. Judgment and debate lead to a program that appears to be sound. Commitment increases to the apparent solution. If the presumed solution actually makes matters worse, the process by which this happens is not evident. So, when the troubles increase, the effects are intensified that are actually worsening the problem.

DYNAMICS OF URBAN SYSTEMS

Our first major excursion outside of corporate policy began in February, 1968, when John F. Collins, former Mayor of Boston, became Professor of Urban Affairs at M.I.T. He and I discussed my work in industrial dynamics and his experience with urban difficulties. A close collaboration led to applying to the dynamics of the city the same methods that had been created for understanding the social and policy structure of the corporation. A model structure was developed to represent the fundamental urban processes. The proposed structure shows how industry, housing, and people interact with each other as a city grows and decays. The results are described in my book *Urban Dynamics,* and some were summarized in *Technology Review* (April, 1969, pp. 21-31).

I had not previously been involved with urban behavior

or urban policies. But the emerging story was strikingly similar to what we had seen in the corporation. Actions taken to alleviate the difficulties of a city can actually make matters worse. We examined four common programs for improving the depressed nature of the central city. One is the creation of jobs as by bussing the unemployed to the suburbs or through governmental jobs as employer of last resort. Second was a training program to increase the skills of the lowest-income group. Third was financial aid to the depressed city as by federal subsidy. Fourth was the construction of low-cost housing. All of these are shown to lie between neutral and detrimental almost irrespective of the criteria used for judgment. They range from ineffective to harmful judged either by their effect on the economic health of the city or by their long-range effect on the low-income population of the city.

The results both confirm and explain much of what has been happening over the last several decades in our cities.

In fact, it emerges that the fundamental cause of depressed areas in the cities comes from *excess* housing in the low-income category rather than the commonly presumed housing shortage. The legal and tax structures have combined to give incentives for keeping old buildings in place. As industrial buildings age, the employment opportunities decline. As residential buildings age, they are used by lower-income groups who are forced to use them at a higher population density. Therefore, jobs decline and population rises while buildings age. Housing, at the higher population densities, accommodates more low-income urban population than can find jobs. A social trap is created where excess low-cost housing beckons low-income people inward because of the available housing. They continue coming to the city until their numbers so far exceed the available income opportunities that the standard of living declines far enough to stop further inflow. Income to the area is then too low to maintain all of the housing. Excess housing falls into disrepair and is abandoned. One can simultaneously have extreme crowding in those buildings that are occupied, while other buildings become excess and are abandoned because the economy of the area can not support all of the residential structures. But the excess residential buildings threaten the area in two ways—they occupy the land so that it cannot be used for job-creating buildings, and they stand ready to accept a rise in population if the area should start to improve economically.

Any change which would otherwise raise the standard of living only takes off the economic pressure momentarily and causes the population to rise enough that the standard of living again falls to the barely tolerable level. A self-regulating system is thereby at work which drives the condition of the depressed area down far enough to stop the increase in people.

At any time, a near-equilibrium exists affecting population mobility between the different areas of the country. To the extent that there is disequilibrium, it means that some area is slightly more attractive than others and population begins to move in the direction of the more attractive area. This movement continues until the rising population drives the more attractive area down in attractiveness until the area is again in equilibrium with its surroundings. Other things being equal, an increase in population of a city crowds housing, overloads job opportunities, causes congestion, increases pollution, encourages crime, and reduces almost every component of the quality of life.

This powerful dynamic force to re-establish an equilibrium in total attractiveness means that any social program must take into account the eventual shifts that will occur in the many components of *attractiveness*. As used here, "attractiveness" is the composite effect of all factors that cause population movement toward or away from an area. Most areas in a country have nearly equal attractiveness most of the time, with only sufficient disequilibrium in attractiveness to account for the shifts in population. But areas can have the same composite attractiveness with different mixes in the components of attractiveness. In one area component A could be high and B low, while the reverse could be true in another area that nevertheless had the same total composite attractiveness. If a program makes some aspect of an area more attractive than its neighbor's, and thereby makes that attractiveness higher momentarily, population of that area rises until other components of attractiveness are driven down far enough to again establish an equilibrium. This means that efforts to improve the condition of our cities will result primarily in increasing the population of the cities and causing the population of the country to concentrate in the cities. The overall condition of urban life, for any particular economic class of population, cannot be appreciably better or worse than that of the remainder of the country to and from which people may come. Programs aimed at improving the city can succeed only if they result in eventually raising the average quality of life of the country as a whole.

ON "RAISING THE QUALITY OF LIFE"

But there is substantial doubt that our urban programs have been contributing to the national quality of life. By concentrating total population, and especially low-income population, in urban locations, undermining the strength and cohesiveness of the community, and making government and bureaucracy so big that the individual feels powerless to influence the system within which he is increasingly constrained, the quality of life is being reduced. In fact, if they have any effect, our efforts to improve our urban areas will in the long run tend to delay the concern about rising total population and thereby contribute directly to the eventual overcrowding of the country and the world.

Any proposed program must deal with both the quality

of life and the factors affecting population. "Raising the quality of life" means releasing stress and pressures, reducing crowding, reducing pollution, alleviating hunger, and treating ill health. But these pressures are exactly the sources of concern and action aimed at controlling total population to keep it within the bounds of the fixed world within which we live. If the pressures are relaxed, so is the concern about how we impinge on the environment. Population will then rise further until the pressures reappear with an intensity that can no longer be relieved. To try to raise quality of life without intentionally creating compensating pressures to prevent a rise in population density will be self-defeating.

Consider the meaning of these interacting attractiveness components as they affect a depressed ghetto area of a city. First we must be clear on the way population density is, in fact, now being controlled. There is some set of forces determining that the density is not far higher or lower than it is. But there are many possible combinations of forces that an urban area can exert. The particular combination will determine the population mix of the area and the economic health of the city. I suggest that the depressed areas of most American cities are created by a combination of forces in which there is a job shortage and a housing excess. The availability of housing draws the lowest-income group until they so far exceed the opportunities of the area that the low standard of living, the frustration, and the crime rate counterbalance the housing availability. Until the pool of excess housing is reduced, little can be done to improve the economic condition of the city. A low-cost housing program alone moves exactly in the wrong direction. It draws more low-income people. It makes the area differentially more attractive to the poor who need jobs and less attractive to those who create jobs. In the new population equilibrium that develops, some characteristic of the social system must compensate for the additional attractiveness created by the low-cost housing. The counterbalance is a further decline of the economic condition for the area. But as the area becomes more destitute, pressures rise for more low-cost housing. The consequence is a downward spiral that draws in the low-income population, depresses their condition, prevents escape, and reduces hope. All of this is done with the best of intentions.

My paper, "Systems Analysis as a Tool for Urban Planning" from a symposium in October, 1969, at the National Academy of Engineering, suggests a reversal of present practice in order to simultaneously reduce the aging housing in our cities and allocate land to income-earning opportunities. The land shifted to industry permits the "balance of trade" of the area to be corrected by allowing labor to create and export a product to generate an income stream with which to buy the necessities of modern life from the outside. But the concurrent reduction of excess housing is absolutely essential. It supplies the land for new jobs. Equally important, the resulting housing shortage creates the population-stabilizing pressure that allows economic revival to proceed without being inundated by rising population. This can all be done without driving the present low-income residents out of the area. It can create *upward economic mobility* to convert the low-income population to a self-supporting basis.

The first reaction of many people to these ideas is to believe that they will never be accepted by elected officials or by residents of depressed urban areas. But some of our strongest support and encouragement is coming from those very groups who are closest to the problems, who see the symptoms first hand, who have lived through the failures of the past, and who must live with the present conditions until enduring solutions are found.

Over the last several decades the country has slipped into a set of attitudes about our cities that are leading to actions that have become an integral part of the system that is generating greater troubles. If we were malicious and wanted to create urban slums, trap low-income people in ghetto areas, and increase the number of people on welfare, we could do little better than follow the present policies. The trend toward stressing income and sales taxes and away from the real estate tax encourages old buildings to remain in place and block self-renewal. The concessions in the income tax laws to encourage low-income housing will in the long run actually increase the total low-income population of the country. The highway expenditures and the government loans for suburban housing have made it easier for higher—income groups to abandon urban areas than to revive them. The pressures to expand the areas incorporated by urban government, in an effort to expand the revenue base, have been more than offset by lowered administrative efficiency, more citizen frustration, and the accelerated decline that is triggered in the annexed areas. The belief that more money will solve urban problems has taken attention away from correcting the underlying causes and has instead allowed the problems to grow to the limit of the available money, whatever that amount might be.*

CHARACTERISTICS OF SOCIAL SYSTEMS

I turn now to some characteristics of social systems that mislead people. These have been identified in our work with corporate and urban systems and from more recent work that I will describe on the world-wide pressures that are now enveloping our planet.

First, social systems are inherently insensitive to most policy changes that people select in an effort to alter the behavior of the system. In fact, a social system tends to draw our attention to the very points at which an attempt to intervene will fail. Our experience, which has been de-

* Our continuing examination of urban behavior has been made possible through a grant to M.I.T. from the Independence Foundation of Philadelphia.

veloped from contact with simple systems, leads us to look close to the symptoms of trouble for a cause. When we look, we discover that the social system presents us with an apparent cause that is plausible according to what we have learned from simple systems. But this apparent cause is usually a coincident occurrence that, like the trouble symptom itself, is being produced by the feedback-loop dynamics of a larger system. For example, as already discussed, we see human suffering in the cities; we observe that it is accompanied (some think caused) by inadequate housing. We increase the housing and the population rises to compensate for the effort. More people are drawn into and trapped in the depressed social system. As another example, the symptoms of excess population are beginning to overshadow the country. These symptoms appear as urban crowding and social pressure. Rather than face the population problem squarely we try to relieve the immediate pressure by planning industry in rural areas and by discussing new towns. If additional urban area is provided it will temporarily reduce the pressures and defer the need to face the underlying population question. The consequence, as it will be seen 25 years hence, will have been to contribute to increasing the population so much that even today's quality of life will be impossible.

A second characteristic of social systems is that all of them seem to have a few sensitive influence points through which the behavior of the system can be changed. These influence points are not in the locations where most people expect. Furthermore, if one identifies in a model of a social system a sensitive point where influence can be exerted, the chances are still that a person guided by intuition and judgment will alter the system in the wrong direction. For example in the urban system, housing is a sensitive control point but, if one wishes to revive the economy of a city and make it a better place for low-income as well as other people, it appears that the amount of low-income housing must be reduced rather than increased. Another example is the world-wide problem of rising population and the disparity between the standards of living in the developed and the underdeveloped countries, an issue arising in the world system to be discussed in the following paragraphs. But it is beginning to appear that a sensitive control point is the rate of generation of capital investment.

And how should one change the rate of capital accumulation? The common answer has been to increase industrialization, but recent examination suggests that hope lies only in reducing the rate of industrialization. This may actually help raise quality of life and contribute to stabilizing population.

As a third characteristic of social systems, there is usually a fundamental conflict between the short-term and long-term consequences of a policy change. A policy which produces improvement in the short run, within five to 10 years, is usually one which degrades the system in the long run, beyond 10 years. Likewise, those policies and programs which produce long-run improvement may initially depress the behavior of the system. This is especially treacherous. The short run is more visible and more compelling. It speaks loudly for immediate attention. But a series of actions all aimed at short-run improvement can eventually burden a system with long-run depressants so severe that even heroic short-run measures no longer suffice. Many of the problems which we face today are the eventual result of short-run measures taken as long as two or three decades ago.

A GLOBAL PERSPECTIVE

I have mentioned social organizations at the corporate level and then touched on work which has been done on the dynamics of the city. Now we are beginning to examine issues of even broader scope.

In July, 1970, we held a two-week international conference on world dynamics. It was a meeting organized for the Club of Rome, a private group of about 50 individuals drawn from many countries who have joined together to attempt a better understanding of social systems at the world level. Their interest lies in the same problems of population, resources, industrialization, pollution, and world-wide disparities of standard of living on which many groups now focus. But the Club of Rome is devoted to taking actions that will lead to a better understanding of world trends and to influencing world leaders and governments. The July meeting at M.I.T. included the general theory and behavior of complex systems and talks on the behavior of specific social systems ranging from corporations through commodity markets to biological systems, drug addiction in the community, and growth and decline of a city. Especially prepared for this conference was a dynamic model of the interactions between world population, industrialization, depletion of natural resources, agriculture, and pollution. A detailed discussion of this world system will soon appear in my book *World Dynamics,* and its further development is the purpose of the "Project on the Predicament of Mankind" being sponsored by the Club of Rome* at M.I.T. for a year under the guidance of Professor Dennis Meadows. The plan is to develop a research group of men from many countries who will eventually base their continuing efforts in a neutral country such as Switzerland. The immediate project will reexamine, verify, alter and extend the preliminary dynamic study of the world system and will relate it to the present world-wide concern about trends in civilization.

The simple model of world interactions as thus far developed shows several different alternative futures depending on whether population growth is eventually suppressed by shortage of natural resources, by pollution, by crowding

*With the generous support of the Volkswagen Foundation in Germany.

and consequent social strife, or by insufficient food. Malthus dealt only with the latter but it is possible for civilization to encounter other controlling pressures before a food shortage occurs.

It is certain that resource shortage, pollution, crowding, food failure, or some other equally powerful force will limit population and industrialization if persuasion and psychological factors do not. Exponential growth cannot continue forever. Our greatest immediate challenge is how we guide the transition from growth to equilibrium. There are many possible mechanisms of growth suppression. That some one or combination will occur is inevitable. Unless we come to understand and to choose, the social system by its internal processes will choose for us. The "natural" mechanisms for terminating exponential growth appear to be the least desirable. Unless we understand and begin to act soon, we may be overwhelmed by a social and economic system we have created but can't control.

Figure 1* shows the structure that has been assumed.

It interrelates the mutual effects of population, capital investment, natural resources, pollution, and the fraction of capital devoted to agriculture. These five system "levels" are shown in the rectangles. Each level is caused to change by the rates of flow in and out, such as the birth rate and death rate that increase and decrease population. As shown by the dotted lines, the five system levels, through intermediate concepts shown at the circles, control the rates of flow. As an example, the death rate at Symbol 10 depends on population P and the "normal" lifetime as stated by death rate normal DRN. But death rate depends also on conditions in other parts of the system. From Circle 12 comes the influence of pollution that here assumes death rate to double if pollution becomes 20 times as severe as in

*All figures are taken from *World Dynamics* by Jay W. Forrester, Wright-Allen Press, 238 Main Street, Cambridge, Massachusetts, 02142, 1971.

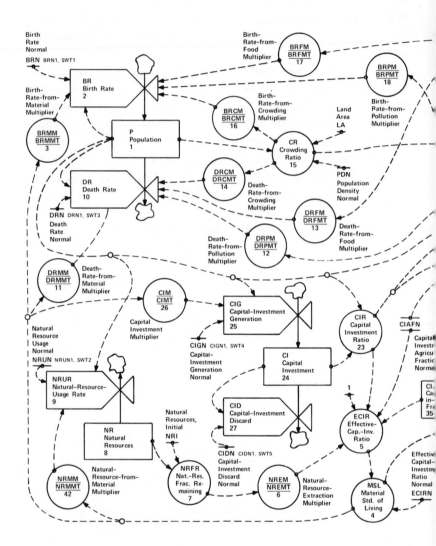

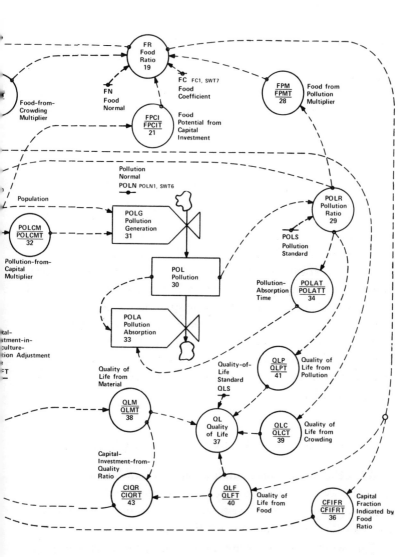

Figure 1. *Upon this world model are based the author's analyses of the effects of changing population and economic growth factors in the next 50 years. It shows the interrelation of population, capital investment, natural resources, pollution, and the fraction of capital devoted to agriculture on which is based the following discussion.*

1970; and, progressively, that death rate would increase
by a factor of 10 if pollution became 60 times as much as
now. Likewise from Circle 13 the effect of food per capita
is to increase death rate as food becomes less available. The
detailed definition of the model states how each rate of flow
is assumed to depend on the levels of population, natural
resources, capital investment, capital devoted to food, and
pollution.

Individually the assumptions in the model are plausible,
create little disagreement, and reflect common discussions
and assertions about the individual responses within the
world system. But each is explicit and can be subjected to
scrutiny. From one viewpoint, the system of Figure 1 is
very simplified. It focuses on a few major factors and omits
most of the sub-structure of world social and economic activity. But from another viewpoint, Figure 1 is comprehensive and complex. The system is far more complete and
the theory described by the accompanying computer model
is much more explicit than the mental models that are now
being used as a basis for world and governmental planning.
It incorporates dozens of nonlinear relationships. The world
system shown here exhibits provocative and even frighten-
ing possibilities.

TRANSITION FROM GROWTH TO EQUILIBRIUM

With the model specified, a computer can be used to show
how the system, as described for each of its parts, would
behave. Given a set of beginning conditions, the computer
can calculate and plot the results that unfold through time.

The world today seems to be entering a condition in
which pressures are rising simultaneously from every one
of the influences that can suppress growth—depleted resources, pollution, crowding, and insufficient food. It is still
unclear which will dominate if mankind continues along

the present path. Figure 2 shows the mode of behavior of this world system given the assumption that pollution reaches a peak and then declines because industrialization is suppressed by falling natural resources. The model system starts with estimates of conditions in 1930. Adjustments have been made so that the generated paths pass through the conditions of 1970.

In Figure 2 the quality of life peaks in the 1950's and by 2020 has fallen far enough to halt further rise in population. Declining resources and the consequent fall in capital investment then exert further pressure to gradually reduce world population.

But we may not be fortunate enough to run gradually out of natural resources. Science and technology may very well find ways to use the more plentiful metals and atomic energy so that resource depletion does not intervene. If so, the way then remains open for some other pressure to arise within the system. Figure 3 shows what happens within this system if the resource shortage is foreseen and avoided. Here the only change from Figure 2 is in the usage rate of natural resources after the year 1970. In Figure 3, resources are used after 1970 at a rate 75 per cent less than assumed in Figure 2. In other words, the standard of living is sustained with a lower drain on the expendable and irreplaceable resources. But the picture is even less attractive! By not running out of resources, population and capital investment are allowed to rise until a pollution crisis is created. Pollution then acts directly to reduce birth rate, increase death rate, and to depress food production. Population which, according to this simple model, peaks at the year 2030 has fallen to one-sixth of the peak population within an interval of 20 years—a world-wide catastrophe of a magnitude never before experienced. Should it occur, one can speculate on which sectors of the world population will suffer most. It is quite possible that the more industrialized countries (which are the ones which have caused such a disaster)

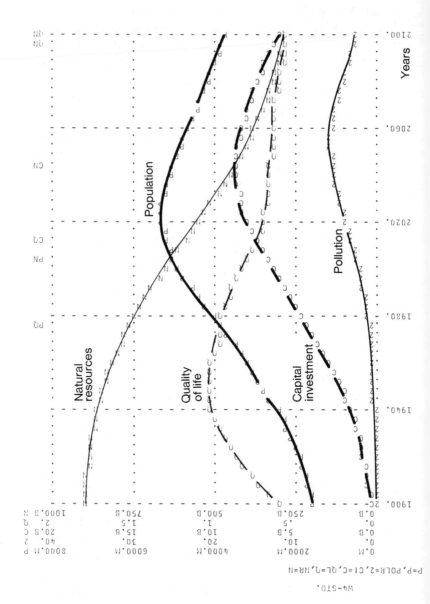

Figure 2. *Basic world model behavior showing the mode in which industrialization and population are suppressed by falling natural resources.*

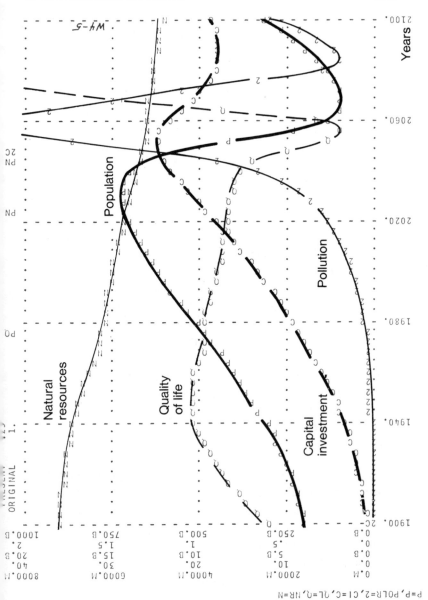

Figure 3. *Pollution crisis precipitated by lower usage rate of natural resources. In 1970 natural resource usage is reduced 75 per cent by more effective technology without affecting material standard of living.*

would be the least able to survive such a disruption to environment and food supply. They might be the ones to take the brunt of the collapse.

Figure 3 shows how a technological success (reducing our dependence on natural resources) can merely save us from one fate only to fall victim to something worse (a pollution catastrophe). There is now developing throughout the world a strong undercurrent of doubt about technology as the savior of mankind. There is a basis for such doubt. Of course, the source of trouble is not technology as such but is instead the management of the entire technological-human-political-economic-natural complex.

Figure 3 is a dramatic example of the general process discussed earlier wherein a program aimed at one trouble symptom results in creating a new set of troubles in some other part of the system. Here the success in alleviating a natural resource shortage throws the system over into the mode of stopping population caused by industrialization which has been freed from natural resource restraint. This process of a solution creating a new problem has defeated many of our past governmental programs and will continue to do so unless we devote more effort to understanding the dynamic behavior of our social systems.

ALTERNATIVES TO DECLINE OR CATASTROPHE

Suppose in the basic world system of Figures 1 and 2 we ask how to sustain the quality of life which is beginning to decline after 1950. One way to attempt this, and it is the way the world is now choosing, might be to increase the rate of industrialization by raising the rate of capital investment. Models of the kind we are here using make such hypothetical questions answerable in a few minutes and at negligible cost. Figure 4 shows what happens if the "normal" rate of capital accumulation is increased by 20 per cent in 1970. The pollution crisis reappears. This time the

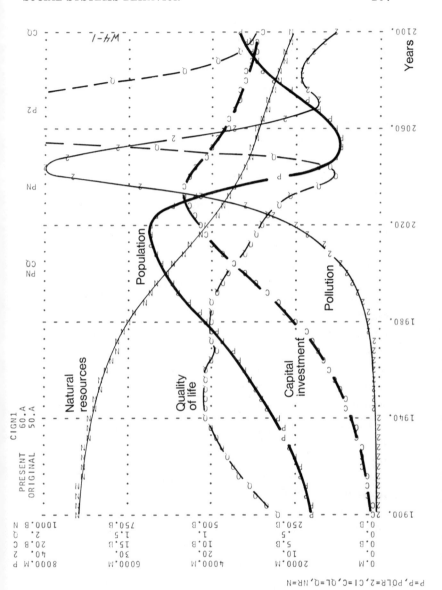

Figure 4. *In 1970 the rate of capital accumulation is increased 20 per cent in an effort to reverse the beginning decline in quality of life. The pollution crisis occurs before natural resources are depleted.*

cause is not the more efficient use of natural resources but the upsurge of industrialization which overtaxes the environment before resource depletion has a chance to depress industrialization. Again, an "obvious" desirable change in policy has caused troubles worse than the ones that were originally being corrected. This is important, not only for its own message but because it demonstrates how an apparently desirable change in a social system can have unexpected and even disastrous results.

Figure 4 should make us cautious about rushing into programs on the basis of short-term humanitarian impulses. The eventual result can be anti-humanitarian. Emotionally inspired efforts often fall into one of three traps set for us by the nature of social systems: The programs are apt to address symptoms rather than causes and attempt to operate through points in the system that have little leverage for change; the characteristic of systems whereby a policy change has the opposite effect in the short run from the effect in the long run can eventually cause deepening difficulties after a sequence of short-term actions; and the effect of a program can be along an entirely different direction than was originally expected, so that suppressing one symptom only causes trouble to burst forth at another point.

Figure 5 retains the 20 per cent additional capital investment rate after 1970 from Figure 4 but in addition explores birth reduction as a way of avoiding crisis. Here the "normal" birth rate has been cut in half in 1970. (Changes in normal rates refer to coefficients which have the specified effect if all other things remain the same. But other things in the system change and also exert their effect on the actual system rates.) The result shows interesting behavior. Quality of life surges upward for 30 years for the reasons that are customarily asserted. Food-per-capita grows, material standard of living rises, and crowding does not become as great. But the more affluent world population continues to use natural resources and to accumulate capital plant at about the same rate as in Figure 4. Load on the environment is more closely related to industrialization than to population and the pollution crisis occurs at about the same point in time as in Figure 4.

Figure 5 shows that the 50 per cent reduction in "normal" birth rate in 1970 was sufficient to start a decline in total population. But the rising quality of life and the reduction of pressures act to start the population curve upward again. This is especially evident in other computer runs where the reduction in "normal" birth rate is not so drastic. Serious questions are raised by this investigation about the effectiveness of birth control as a means of controlling population. The secondary consequence of starting a birth control program will be to increase the influences that raise birth rate and reduce the apparent pressures that require population control. A birth control program which would be effective, all other things being equal, may largely fail because other things will not remain equal. Its very incipient success can set in motion forces to defeat the program.

Figure 6 combines the reduced resource usage rate and the increased capital investment rate of Figures 3 and 4. The result is to make the population collapse occur slightly sooner and more severely. To the modified system of Figure 6, Figure 7 then examines the result if technology finds ways to reduce the pollution generated by a given degree of industrialization. Here in Figure 7, the pollution rate, other things being the same, is reduced by 50 per cent from that in Figure 6. The result is to postpone the day of reckoning by 20 years and to allow the world population to grow 25 per cent greater before the population collapse occurs. The "solution" of reduced pollution has, in effect, caused more people to suffer the eventual consequences. Again we see the dangers of partial solutions. Actions at one point in a system that attempt to relieve one kind of distress produce an unexpected result in some other part of the system. If the interactions are not sufficiently understood, the conse-

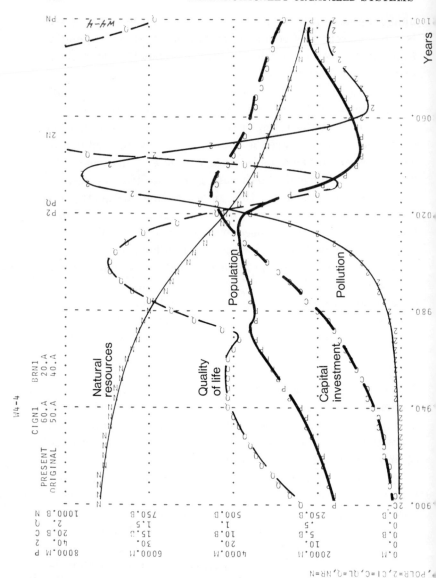

Figure 5. *In 1970 the 20 per cent increase in capital accumulation of Figure 4 is retained and "normal" birth rate is reduced 50 per cent. Capital investment continues to grow until the pollution crisis develops. After an initial decline, population is again pushed up by the rapid rise in quality of life that precedes the collapse.*

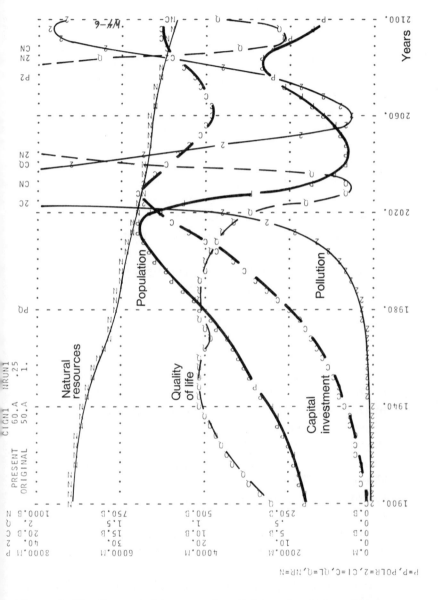

Figure 6. *The 20 per cent increase of capital investment from Figure 4 and the 75 per cent reduction of natural resource usage from Figure 3 are combined.*

quences can be as bad or worse than those that led to the initial action.

There are no utopias in our social systems. There appear to be no sustainable modes of behavior that are free of pressures and stresses. But there are many possible modes and some are more desirable than others. Usually, the more attractive kinds of behavior in our social systems seem to be possible only if we have a good understanding of the system dynamics and are willing to endure the self-discipline and pressures that must accompany the desirable mode. The world system of Figure 1 can exhibit modes that are more hopeful than the crises of the earlier figures. But to develop the more promising modes will require restraint and dedication to a long-range future that man may not be capable of sustaining.

Figure 8 shows the world system if several policy changes are adopted together in the year 1970. Population is stabilized. Quality of life rises about 50 per cent. Pollution remains at about the 1970 level. Would such a world be accepted? It implies an end to population increase and economic growth.

In Figure 8 the normal rate of capital accumulation is *reduced* 40 per cent from its previous value. The "normal" birth rate is reduced 50 per cent from its earlier value. The "normal" pollution generation is reduced 50 per cent from the value before 1970. The "normal" rate of food production is *reduced* 20 per cent from its previous value. (These changes in "normal" values are the changes for a specific set of system conditions. Actual system rates continue to be affected by the varying conditions of the system.) But reduction in investment rate and reduction in agricultural emphasis are counterintuitive and not likely to be discovered or accepted without extensive system studies and years of argument—perhaps more years than are available. The changes in pollution generation and natural resource usage may be easier to understand and to achieve. The severe reduction in world-wide birth rate is the most doubtful. Even if technical and biological methods existed, the improved condition of the world might remove the incentive for sustaining the birth reduction emphasis and discipline.

FUTURE POLICY ISSUES

The dynamics of world behavior bear directly on the future of the United States. American urbanization and industrialization are a major part of the world scene. The United States is setting a pattern that other parts of the world are trying to follow. That pattern is not sustainable. Our foreign policy and our overseas commercial activity seem to be running contrary to overwhelming forces that are developing in the world system. The following issues are raised by the preliminary investigations to date. They must, of course, be examined more deeply and confirmed by more thorough research into the assumptions about structure and detail of the world system.

• Industrialization may be a more fundamentally disturbing force in world ecology than is population. In fact, the population explosion is perhaps best viewed as a result of technology and industrialization. I include medicine and public health as a part of industrialization.

• Within the next century, man may be facing choices from a four-pronged dilemma—suppression of modern industrial society by a natural resource shortage, collapse of world population from changes wrought by pollution, population limitation by food shortage, or population control by war, disease, and social stresses caused by physical and psychological crowding.

• We may now be living in a "golden age" where, in spite of the world-wide feeling of malaise, the quality of life is, on the average, higher than ever before in history and higher now than the future offers.

• Efforts for direct population control may be inherently

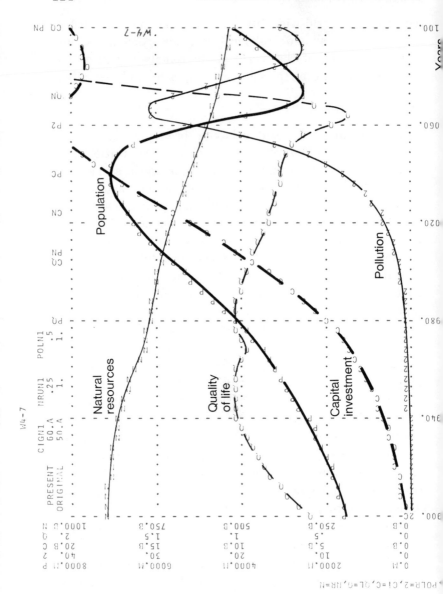

Figure 7. *Increased capital investment rate and reduced natural resource usage from Figure 6 are retained. In addition in 1970 the normal" rate of pollution generation is reduced 50 per cent. The effect of pollution control is to allow population to grow 25 per cent further and to delay the pollution crisis by 20 years.*

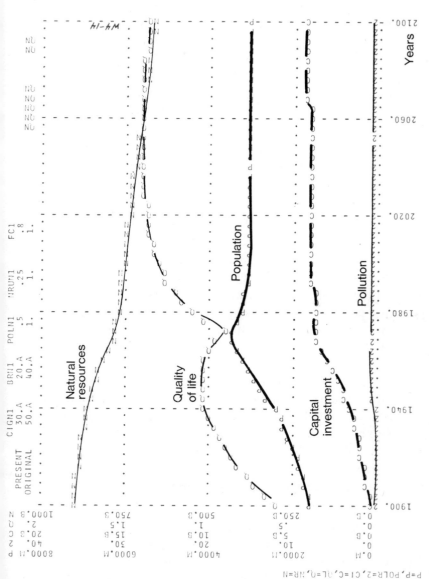

Figure 8. *One set of conditions that establishes a world equilibrium. In 1970 capital investment rate is reduced 40 per cent, birth rate is reduced 50 per cent, pollution generation is reduced 50 per cent, natural resources usage rate is reduced 75 per cent, and food production is reduced 20 per cent.*

self-defeating. If population control begins to result as hoped in higher per capita food supply and material standard of living, these very improvements can generate forces to trigger a resurgence of population growth.

• The high standard of living of modern industrial societies seems to result from a production of food and material goods that has been able to outrun the rising population. But, as agriculture reaches a space limit, as industrialization reaches a natural-resource limit, and as both reach a pollution limit, population tends to catch up. Population then grows until the "quality of life" falls far enough to generate sufficiently large pressures to stabilize population.

• There may be no realistic hope for the present underdeveloped countries reaching the standard of living demonstrated by the present industrialized nations. The pollution and natural resource load placed on the world environmental system by each person in an advanced country is probably 10-20 times greater than the load now generated by a person in an underdeveloped country. With four times as much population in underdeveloped countries as in the present developed countries, their rising to the economic level of the United States could mean an increase of 10 times in the natural resource and pollution load on the world environment. Noting the destruction that has already occurred on land, in the air, and especially in the oceans, no capability appears to exist for handling such a rise in standard of living for the present total population of the world.

• A society with a high level of industrialization may be nonsustainable. It may be self-extinguishing if it exhausts the natural resources on which it depends. Or, if unending substitution for declining natural resources is possible, the international strife over "pollution and environmental rights" may pull the average world-wide standard of living back to the level of a century ago.

• From the long view of a hundred years hence, the present efforts of underdeveloped countries to industrialize along Western patterns may be unwise. They may now be closer to the ultimate equilibrium with the environment than are the industrialized nations. The present underdeveloped countries may be in a better condition for surviving the forthcoming world-wide environmental and economic pressures than are the advanced countries. When one of the several forces materializes that is strong enough to cause a collapse in world population, the advanced countries may suffer far more than their share of the decline.

A NEW FRONTIER

It is now possible to take hypotheses about the separate parts of a social system, to combine them in a computer model, and to learn the consequences. The hypotheses may at first be no more correct than the ones we are using in our intuitive thinking. But the process of computer modeling and model testing requires these hypotheses to be stated more explicitly. The model comes out of the hazy realm of the mental model into an unambiguous model or statement to which all have access. Assumptions can then be checked against all available information and can be rapidly improved. The great uncertainty with mental models is the inability to anticipate the consequences of interactions between the parts of a system. This uncertainty is totally eliminated in computer models. Given a stated set of assumptions, the computer traces the resulting consequences without doubt or error. This is a powerful procedure for clarifying issues. It is not easy. Results will not be immediate.

We are on the threshold of a great new era in human pioneering. In the past there have been periods characterized by geographical exploration. Other periods have dealt with the formation of national governments. At other times the focus was on the creation of great literature. Most recently we have been through the pioneering frontier of science and technology. But science and technology are now a routine part of our life. Science is no longer a frontier. The process of scientific discovery is orderly and organized.

I suggest that the next frontier for human endeavor is to pioneer a better understanding of the nature of our social systems. The means are visible. The task will be no easier than the development of science and technology. For the next 30 years we can expect rapid advance in understanding the complex dynamics of our social systems. To do so will require research, the development of teaching methods and materials, and the creation of appropriate educational programs. The research results of today will in one or two decades find their way into the secondary schools just as concepts of basic physics moved from research to general education over the past three decades.

What we do today fundamentally affects our future two or three decades hence. If we follow intuition, the trends of the past will continue into deepening difficulty. If we set up research and educational programs, which are now possible but which have not yet been developed, we can expect a far sounder basis for action.

THE NATION'S REAL ALTERNATIVES

The record to date implies that our people accept the future growth of United States population as preordained, beyond the purview and influence of legislative control, and as a ground rule which determines the nation's task as finding cities in which the future population can live. But I have been describing the circular processes of our social system in which there is no unidirectional cause and effect but instead a ring of actions and consequences that close back on themselves. One could say, incompletely, that the population will grow and that cities, space, and food must be provided. But one can likewise say, also incompletely, that the provision of cities, space and food will cause the population to grow. Population generates pressure for urban growth, but urban pressures help to limit population.

Population grows until stresses rise far enough, which is to say that the quality of life falls far enough, to stop further increase. Everything we do to reduce those pressures causes the population to rise farther and faster and hastens the day when expediencies will no longer suffice. The United States is in the position of a wild animal running from its pursuers. We still have some space, natural resources, and agricultural land left. We can avoid the question of rising population as long as we can flee into this bountiful reservoir that nature provided. But it is obvious that the reservoirs are limited. The wild animal usually flees until he is cornered, until he has no more space. Then he turns to fight, but he no longer has room to maneuver. He is less able to forestall disaster than if he had fought in the open while there was still room to yield and to dodge. The United States is running away from its long-term threats by trying to relieve social pressures as they arise. But if we persist in treating only the symptoms and not the causes, the result will be to increase the magnitude of the ultimate threat and reduce our capability to respond when we no longer have space to flee.

What does this mean? Instead of automatically accepting the need for new towns and the desirability of locating industry in rural areas, we should consider confining our cities. If it were possible to prohibit the encroachment by housing and industry onto even a single additional acre of farm and forest, the resulting social pressures would hasten the day when we stabilize population. Some European countries are closer to realizing the necessity of curtailing urban growth than are we. As I understand it, farm land surrounding Copenhagen cannot be used for either residence or industry until the severest of pressures forces the government to rezone small additional parcels. When land is rezoned, the corresponding rise in land price is heavily taxed to remove the incentive for land speculation. The waiting time for an empty apartment in Copenhagen may be years. Such pressures certainly cause the Danes to face the population problem more squarely than do we.

Our greatest challenge now is how to handle the transition from growth into equilibrium. Our society has behind it 1000 years of tradition that has encouraged and rewarded growth. The folklore and the success stories praise growth and expansion. But that is not the path of the future. Many of the present stresses in our society are from the pressures that always accompany the conversion from growth into equilibrium.

In our studies of social systems, we have made a number of investigations of life cycles that start with growth and merge into equilibrium. There are always severe stresses in the transition. Pressures must rise far enough to suppress the forces that produced growth. Not only do we face the pressure that will stop the population growth; we also encounter pressures that will stop the rise of industrialization and standard of living. The social stresses will rise. The economic forces will be ones for which we have no precedent. The psychological forces will be beyond those for which we are prepared. Our studies of urban systems demonstrated how the pressures from shortage of land and rising unemployment accompany the usual transition from urban growth to equilibrium. But the pressures we have seen in our cities are minor compared to those which the nation is approaching. The population pressures and the economic forces in a city that was reaching equilibrium have in the past been able to escape to new land areas. But that escape is becoming less possible. Until now we have had, in effect, an inexhaustible supply of farm land and food-growing potential But now we are reaching the critical point where, all at the same time, population is overrunning productive land, agricultural land is almost fully employed for the first time, the rise in population is putting more demand on the food supplies, and urbanization is pushing agriculture out of the fertile areas into the marginal lands. For the first time demand is rising into a condition where supply will begin to fall while need increases. The crossover from plenty to shortage can occur abruptly.

The fiscal and monetary system of the country is a complex social-economic-financial system of the kind we have been discussing. It is clear the country is not agreed on behavior of the interactions between government policy, growth, unemployment, and inflation. An article by a writer for *Finance* Magazine in July, 1970, suggests that the approach I have been discussing be applied in fiscal and monetary policy and their relationships to the economy. I estimate that such a task would be only a few times more difficult than was the investigation of urban growth and stagnation. The need to accomplish it becomes more urgent as the economy begins to move for the first time from a history of growth into the turbulent pressures that will accompany the transition from growth to one of the many possible kinds of equilibrium. We need to choose the kind of equilibrium before we arrive.

In a hierarchy of systems, there is usually a conflict between the goals of a subsystem and the welfare of the broader system. We see this in the urban system. The goal of the city is to expand and to raise its quality of life. But this increases population, industrialization, pollution, and demands on food supply. The broader social system of the country and the world requires that the goals of the urban areas be curtailed and that the pressures of such curtailment become high enough to keep the urban areas and population within the bounds that are satisfactory to the larger system of which the city is a part. If this nation chooses to continue to work for some of the traditional urban goals, and if it succeeds, as it may well do, the result will be to deepen the distress of the country as a whole and eventually to deepen the crisis in the cities themselves. We may be at the point where higher pressures in the present are necessary if insurmountable pressures are to be avoided in the future.

I have tried to give you a glimpse of the nature of multi-loop feedback systems, a class to which our social systems belong. I have attempted to indicate how these systems mislead us because our intuition and judgment have been formed to expect behavior different from that actually possessed by such systems. I believe that we are still pursuing national programs that will be at least as frustrating and futile as many of the past. But there is hope we can now begin to understand the dynamic behavior of our social systems. Progress will be slow. There are many crosscurrents in the social sciences which will cause confusion and delay. The approach that I have been describing is very different from the emphasis on data-gathering and statistical analysis that occupies much of the time of social research. But there have been breakthroughs in several areas. If we proceed expeditiously but thoughtfully, there is a basis for optimism.

SUGGESTED READINGS

Jay W. Forrester, *Industrial Dynamics*. Cambridge: The M.I.T. Press, 1961.

Jay W. Forrester, *Urban Dynamics*. Cambridge: The M.I.T. Press, 1969.

Jay W. Forrester, *Principles of Systems*, Wright-Allen Press, 1968, 238 Main St., Cambridge, Mass. 02142.

Jay W. Forrester, *World Dynamics*, Wright-Allen Press, 1971, 238 Main St., Cambridge, Mass. 02142.

Dennis L. Meadows, *Dynamics of Commodity Production Cycles*, Wright-Allen Press, 1970, 238 Main St., Cambridge, Mass. 02142.

Planning and Human Action

Hasan Ozbekhan

University of Pennsylvania

I. INTRODUCTION

Planning is not a validated body of knowledge. It has no theory. Its factual documentation is sparse and fragmentary —descriptive of special experiences that cannot rightfully be generalized. It is, so to speak, a tree that is all branches and no trunk.

With subjects of this kind, everything one writes tends to meander into hazy speculations. Consequently one tries, almost instinctively, to organize one's thoughts by using some a priori framework that will provide a few guideline rules of composition, the first of which is to start from the very beginning, no matter how seemingly unimportant that initial step may be.

I shall follow that rule by focusing the discussion on the proposition that *planning is a rationally organized, consciously future-directed human action system.* To validate this proposition we will need first to define and describe human action in its relevant aspects and discover its systemic structure and characteristics. Then, we shall have to relate our findings to the idea of planning and thus to try to discover what that idea means in terms of human action.

To help us do this I shall invent and constantly refer to two simple examples—the simplest I can think of. Admittedly, this approach diverges from the usual, but the subject is complicated and I feel that such examples can be of aid in establishing a connective line along which the arguments may be strung. Step by step, I will try to elaborate the notions and ideas that the examples bring to mind. And

Illustrations of this chapter on pages 219-230.

throughout this probably difficult journey I will join the reader, not only in wandering with him among concepts and their offshoots, but also in seeking whatever hypotheses and (hopefully) conclusions, the quest for a better understanding of the nature of planning may lead us to.

The examples I have chosen describe two similar occurrences. For them to have meaning, the writer and the reader will have to stretch their imaginations, and while remaining in the second half of the twentieth century, try to visualize the world of man in its early stages, at that moment when he had just begun to be conscious of his self, of his distinct identity. Whether this psychologically conditioned statement is accurate, or whether such a moment did, in fact, occur historically, I don't know. All I want to convey is that the first event we will observe in our mind's eye takes place at the very dawn of human experience—before man knew how to make tools.

Let us set the background. Evening is coming, and at the edge of the primeval forest we see a creature who, although he doesn't quite resemble us, we would nevertheless call a man. He is walking; he stops. He picks up a rock almost the size of his hand. Then he goes on. Soon we can no longer see him. He has entered the forest, and besides, it's too dark now. The sun has set.

Our second example, an occurrence almost identical to the first, possesses one immense difference: many millenia have passed, and with them, many generations. Once more we are at the edge of the primeval forest, and we note that nothing in these natural surroundings has changed. The earth, or world, is the same as when we first saw it. For symmetry's sake, let us again say it is evening—the sun low on the horizon, the shadows in the open spaces, long. A man is walking, hugging the tree-line. This time we immediately recognize him as one of us, although we might call him "primitive." He resembles pictures we have seen labeled "Neolithic Hunter." He's more or less dressed in furs;

whereas the creature we shall take to have been his ancestor was almost, or wholly, naked. Since he appears to be hurrying we deduce he is going somewhere (to a settlement, a group, tribe, family?), and wants to get there before nightfall. But suddenly he stops, bends down and picks up a stone. He examines it for a moment. We will say that he does this to make sure it is sylex—the kind of hard, yet flaky stone which by chipping, and perhaps rubbing afterwards, he may be able to convert into some sort of tool: an axe head, for instance. He hurries on. After a moment he disappears into the forest at a point where there may be something resembling a path. We can't be sure, for now it's become quite dark. This has all happened very fast.

These then, are the *observable facts* from which we shall proceed.

II. HUMAN ACTION MODELS

a. Elaboration and Interpretation of the Examples

The two occurrences we have witnessed in our mind's eye are instances of human action. If they are to serve the purposes of this paper we must now go beyond, or beneath, what we saw, draw the pertinent distinctions between the two events, and try to understand what actually took place. We can do this by delineating a meaningful context for each case, and then trying to evolve "models"—*human action models*—that will enable us eventually to talk about planning. Since we are bound to observe and describe everything in terms of the language and perception that our own time imposes upon us, our elaboration will necessarily contain a great deal of interpretation. We can only hope the interpretation will not deeply distort the meaning of what we have observed.

When we looked, not at our actors, but at the *environment* that was surrounding them, which in both instances we can call Nature without fear of sounding presumptuous, we noticed that despite the millenia intervening between our first and second examples, this environment had not visibly changed. And from our perspective we know that it will change very slowly—yield very slowly to the action of man. Therefore, it seems reasonable to assume that to both our very early ancestor and the hunter, the environment appeared virtually the same. It was the all-encompassing, embedding milieu in which they had to survive. From it they drew everything that was necessary for survival in its most total sense. And, although intellectually they did not understand the (still very weak) *inter*activity that existed between them and their environment, they experienced it and responded to it. They may not have known, but we do know that Nature is an immensely complex set of conditions existing and evolving in a dynamic state of ecological balance; that if any of these conditions were to change sufficiently men would also have to change so as to adapt to what would be a different environment; and that if, in the time of our ancestors, conditions had changed drastically, or too rapidly, adaptation might have become impossible, and the particular form of life man embodies might not have survived.

Although our actors were ignorant of these contingencies, they had probably noticed that the world which surrounded them possessed both regularities and, at times catastrophic, discontinuities. Days and nights did alternate; seasons did follow each other according to some mysteriously ordered pattern; birds did migrate and return; animals as well as men did follow in the wake of other animals they fed on; certain types of food became exhausted and both men and animals had either to move elsewhere or discover other kinds of nutriments; and so on. On the other hand, some occurrences must have appeared to early man as belonging to a different order of magnitude and consequence—though still part of the natural unfolding of events. Lightning struck suddenly and whole forests burned; caves crumbled under torrential rains which also flooded the hunting grounds; other animals—looking very like oneself—sometimes attacked and killed you. And always, even under the best of circumstances, food was scarce, difficult and dangerous to secure. Predatory beasts hunted *you*, and often seemed stronger, faster, better armed and more fully endowed for survival than your own kind.

To the mind of early man (again speaking from our own perspective), the environment must have seemed utterly baffling, being possessed of two basic and antithetical characteristics: rhythms, regularities, and a certain reassuring repetitiveness; then, arhythmic occurrences, irregularities, and sporadic, fearsome, survival-threatening events. In certain respects the environment appeared to be *organized;* in others, disordered. It was both predictable and unpredictable. Order was particularly visible in the more fundamental events, such as seasonal succession, about which man could do nothing. Disorder, on the whole, was most powerfully manifest in daily immediacies: the perilous search for scarce food, the dangers, unforseen and unforseeable, that beset man on all sides—events affecting man fully, personally, and continually. About these could man do something?

We ask this on the supposition that early man might have noticed a rather subtle and curious fact; namely, that living amid disorder in the immediacies and adapting to it did not mean to exist with it on *its* terms, but rather to cope with it, act on it, impose *his* terms upon it insofar as possible. The one thing the environment did not seem to allow was passivity. Constant action, relentless and directed activity must have appeared to be one of the inescapable requirements for survival. And over time, such activity doubtless took many forms: increasingly risky endeavors, long chances, thinking of tomorrow's situation as well as of today's. For, unless man acted in these various new ways, something strange happened: the disorder that closely surrounded him increased, at least it appeared to him to be increasing, and that he was losing his hold. Given such conditions, it is clear that the actors of our examples and their kinsmen had to spend virtually all their energy in adaptation, in striving against what we might call the environment's "disorder."

Here, let us return to the first example and follow it up, not from the standpoint of psychological motivation, for that would be impossible, but with reference to acts.

As we watch Early Man, our first actor, pick up a rock during those gray hours of oncoming night, let us assume that he does this without any explicit idea of what he will do with it. We said that the rock was about the size of his hand; and now, we can speculate that in a moment of sudden insight he realizes that with that heavy, jagged object in his hand, he is more effective in defense, aggression, or in pounding food he might eat. As yet he has no notion of what we call an axe, or of any other kind of tool. Still, that rock in the hand has improved his immediate circumstances. The improvement was minimal, but his recognizing that it was, or might be, an improvement was a tremendous event. With this simple recognition, he enlarged the possibilities for his own and his kind's long-term survival to an incalculable degree. For when the first attempts at using the rock do indeed extend his effectiveness, the use of such rough rocks will become an almost ineradicable and transmittable part of the human experience.

In our terminology, we may say that he has already succeeded, though barely, in tilting the metabolic balance between himself and the environment in his favor. And in the temporal sense, namely, insofar as the future is concerned, he has opened up a vast sphere of potential applications, all deriving from that small new power the rock in the hand gave him.

While this modest act owes its importance primarily to its implicit consequences, it has considerable import of its own. Beneath its surface we can already discern of pattern of underlying facts that I shall try to portray in Figure 1, on the next page.

In this diagram I have distinguished two sets of elements as components of the *action model*. The first set: perception of reality, ends, and recognition of usefulness represent what we might call "given behavior stimuli;" the second: knowledge, possible future applications are less clear cut. The graphic symbols in the first set overlap because I am not sure that our actor does, as yet, differentiate his circumstances (perception of reality) from his instinctual striving for survival (ends), or the latter from his having recognized something as being useful. We assume, as I believe we should, that these stimuli exist simultaneously. They form an undifferentiated continuum in his mind.

Unlike the first, the second set of elements is temporally removed from the action, and it is also causally uncertain. Knowledge to be derived from the use of the rock, and possible future applications of that object exist only as potentialities. The chances of their being actualized are, among other things, a function of the actor's individual temperament, of the imitative capacities of the group members, and perhaps more pertinently, of the number of similar actions taking place throughout the environment. Both sets of elements are of course interconnected. The creative element is found primarily in *recognition*, and is then projected into "knowledge," and into whatever other applications might evolve from recognition and the ensuing action.

It is evident that this type of action does not directly express what we, today, call "planning," except perhaps, in the dim realization of the stone's possible usefulness in the struggle for survival. However, we might argue that some embryonic, or implicit, or latent kind of planning does inhere to the decision to pick up the rock, for, given the right circumstances, the future of the man with a stone in his hand will be different from the future of those who have

not thought of picking up such stones. It is further implicit
in the possibility of evolving different applications of the
stone, and in the knowledge that can derive from these
applications and be increased by them.

What we have in this action model is probably a pre-
creative act. On the surface, at least, it could be mere
accident; hence it does not correspond to true planned action, but to action arising instinctually or from sub-conscious insights. However, in all such actions, the entire
information base needed for planning is in the process of
becoming crystallized. Let us, then, for a moment look at
this process of crystallization.

Since we know that, historically, the evolution from the
stone to the tool actually did take place, we can speculate
about the transition and in doing so, borrow an analogical
action pattern from cybernetics. Experiments have shown
us that a servo-mechanism with sensors and a built-in memory advances by means of trials and error-corrections when
placed within a maze. The process is very slow, and the
time spent in making its way through the maze is extremely
long. Yet, with each error-correction the response time of
the system becomes shorter. Learning occurs.

If we strengthen the analogy this experiment offers us
by referring to observations and hypotheses taken from the
metabolic behavior of living cells and the formation of the
metabolism/enzyme/gene complex[1], it suggests to us that
before Early Man had the creative impulse that led him
to pick up the stone and use it, many millenia had passed
since the origin of human life. And after that event had
occurred, uncounted generations must have continued to
live in virtually the same state as before—in vulnerable and
fearsome contact with the environment. However, this latter
interval of time is qualitatively different from the preceed-

---

[1] A. I. Oparin, *L'Origine de la Vie*, Editions de la Paix, Moscow,
1963. See also, P. Idatte, *La Révolution Cybernetique*, Cours de
l'I.N.S.A., Lyon, 1961.

ing one. For now, during this second long time-span, what we called the "possible future applications" of the stone have become a part of reality.

To illustrate, as well as to take a step forward, it is easy to imagine that as stones and rocks came into more general usage, someone might have noted that sharp edged rocks were more effective than blunt ones since they could be used for cutting as well as pounding. Here again, we are dealing with action that is creative. Its creativity could have become manifest either in *noticing* the effectiveness of sharp edged rocks and thereafter looking for them—a variant of creativity-as-recognition—or in realizing that pieces of rock, whatever their shape, could be given edges and made sharp if one acted upon them in appropriate ways, if one *transformed* them.

The form of creativity that involved the realization that one could transform objects, we would no longer call an accident but "invention." In the evolution of an action model, this corresponds to a culmination. At this stage our model can be depicted as in Figure 2.

In this diagram the action already occurs against a rather complex background of system elements. "Perception of reality" can now be shown separately, for we can begin to assume that the actor is already able to differentiate between his "self," and the various categories and levels of events that we shall call his "circumstances." Although he is part of these circumstances, in that Nature remains his context, he has reached the point where he can act upon some— a very limited number—of these circumstances. He can sharpen stones to serve certain defined "ends," of which survival is still the overriding one; yet the very meaning of survival has become enlarged. Our actor's knowledge of the possible applications of his sharpened stone or tool, allow him now to regard survival as something that can be achieved in a variety of ways through different uses of the tool. He may not yet be able wholly to articulate these ways, hence his "objectives" remain confused with ends. Nevertheless "purpose," i.e. that stones must be sharpened to attain certain differentiated and known ends, can be said to have entered his consciousness. The same pertains to "goal;" he is aware of a specific preferred outcome of his action—the sharpened stone. What remains fuzzy are the "means" for sharpening the stone. Probably he does it still rather haphazardly. He has had the idea, and this interests us most for the moment, but has he discovered the most efficient manner of translating idea into object?

Also unclear are the "possible future applications." Early man now possesses a sharpened stone. Whether he is aware that by sharpening similar stones in different ways, shaping them into varied forms, he can achieve a large number of different objectives more easily, we do not know. But the evolutionary momentum is operating already, and the information loop can be seen as closed. Possible variations of the sharp-edged stone can henceforth feed into our actor's "knowledge" and expand it. This, in turn, both alters, and is informed by, the expanding range of his ends. And although it remains a question of time (accelerating time, now before multiple applications of varied sharp-edged tools will be worked out, and efficient means to make them will become part of our actor's action system, we do have what could well be the most difficult and rare component of an action system: *creativity*. How that creativity came to manifest itself is irrelevant to us. What we know is that further evolution of this particular line of action will only yield *derived inventions,* and especially *innovations*. We will not again be confronted with a first and unique exemplar, an *original;* we shall have *copies* and whatever is needed to make them. But regardless of how highly variegated the forms or appearances of these copies, that single, initial and basic idea which generated the entire evolution will underlie them all.

Reviewing the significant aspects of this creative stage,

we find: the time interval between the initial act and the emergence of any concrete result extremely long, and the process slow, being one of trial and error and groping; causal relationships, of a linear or deterministic kind, untraceable; objectives, blurred; the fan of alternative potential outcomes, extensive; choice procedures purely intuitive, almost sub-conscious; any specific outcome, uncertain; and the means for advancing toward any outcome, tentative and improvised.

In modern terminology such an action pattern would correspond to what is called "decision making under true uncertainty"—although I am aware that in our examples we did not refer to any interlinking decisions.

In sum three highly important features define the kind of creative action system we have been trying to outline: (i) the fact that all the information is gathered at the end of the processes that the system governs; (ii) the fact that as an evolutionary process it is complete in itself, and possesses some sort of finality; (iii) the fact that, if successful in reaching an outcome, it establishes those conditions that are necessary for accelerating future action processes that will be derived from it.

In this main stage of creative action, that of the deliberate transformation of the stone, certain fundamental characteristics of planning begin to emerge. We have definite knowledge that a stone can, under certain conditions, be transformed—be given a sharp edge; that because of the time interval this transformation requires, the sharp edged stone is a future state of the initial stone, and is also the outcome that the action system strives to achieve; that the end (survival) is served by such an outcome and that, consequently, the value which inheres to this end becomes translated into that outcome. Since the sharp edged stone has altered the circumstances of the man who has it and knows how to use it—that is, since he can better control his environment—his perception of reality has changed. Finally, he is now capable of assuming that as long as he finds stones he can sharpen, his life will be easier. Some of his actions have become directed, and are guided by his "purpose."

Obviously, we don't have the whole of planned action. Our actor does not yet have to choose among equally valuable alternatives either insofar as his ends are concerned (survival remains unique), or his objectives (he has not yet worked out the range of potential applications of the stone). Nevertheless, we have a partial form of planned action.

Meanwhile knowledge about other functions and applications of the sharp edge must be assumed to be growing, and although many generations will pass between the invention of the sharp edge and its differentiated uses, we can hurdle this time interval, and return to the spot at the edge of the forest where we know we shall meet the Neolithic Hunter of our second example.

He is there, near the tree line, stooping to pick up that piece of rock. He assures himself that it is sylex, then disappears into the darkening forest.

Several things immediately strike us. Unlike his ancestor, our Neolithic Hunter did not pick up the rock on mere impulse; his was a deliberate act. He even knew that he wanted sylex, for he had been taught it was better than other rocks for chipping or shaping into various tools. This knowledge had been transmitted to him either by family elders or those in his group who had the function of passing on learning from one generation to the next.

To give our hunter a firmer identity, we may say that he belongs to a distinguishable social setting; he holds certain beliefs in common with the other members of his society; he acts in accordance with a number of established traditions; and, in relation to his social context, he is required to play several roles—hunter, head of family, fighter, etc.

We can assume that, by now, the creation of our hunter's ancestors (the sharp edge) has been fully "operationalized."

He has all the necessary knowledge to transform sylex into those tools with which he is acquainted—those about which his group can provide information. In short, the means for making certain things have been worked out. The means consist of *rules* that are transmitted to him, and of the *skills* that such rules govern. His development of these skills depends on his individual talents and endowments. Once our hunter is capable of making alternative tools, he has several options available to him, and must determine particular *objectives*. Before he starts to work he is obliged to make rudimentary strategic decisions. Hence, his action model should look like the one I have sketched in Figure 3.

This model contains the elements of human action that can now be explicated, with increasing reference to planned action, and to planning.

b. *Fundamental Elements and Concepts.*

As a whole the model in Figure 3 represents a system, or to be more precise, two systems: the system of human action, and the system of the external environment (the latter is barely indicated in the diagram). The two overlap. Human action impinges upon the environment in the form of consequences, and the environment impinges upon human action in terms of perceived reality. We shall, therefore, have to deal with both systems simultaneously. But first let us consider the notion of system itself.

1. *The Concept of System*

In the lead article of this book Paul Weiss has provided us with a very complete and probing treatment of the concept of "system."* The reader is, therefore, invited to review that analysis at this point so that he may approach the discussion that follows—which is rather more limited in scope for being directed specifically to human action and to planning—having in mind a fully elaborated idea of what

*See especially, Section V, "WHAT IS A SYSTEM?"

the notion of "system" represents, both substantively and methodologically.

At the highest level of generality:

(1) "A system is a set of interrelated elements."[1]

While it is true that the individual elements of a system are named and defined separately, reasoning about systems is directed to the whole system rather than to its component parts. In such a holistic method, the emphasis rests on total system behavior. The aim of what is generally called the "systems approach" is to draw conclusions regarding an entire system through an understanding of the relationships between elements and the properties of their interactions. Moreover, system is a concept that can accommodate any qualifier one chooses (e.g. abstract system, concrete system, causal system, purposeful system, dynamic system, action system, planning system, social system, etc.) without its structural characteristics being affected. Elements of a system can denote concepts, objects, or operations; they can also represent the conceptualization of objects or operations.

In human action and in planning, the system elements include conceptualizations as well as objects. Moreover, as we shall see later, in the case of planning, the total system is hierarchical. This means that its elements are grouped together within discrete levels which, while forming independent systems, have nevertheless inter-level relationships that govern and control the behavior of the total system.

Given these very cursory clarifications, we can now discuss the various elements of the action system shown in Figure 3, pointing out at each step their relevance to, or connection with, planning.

[1] R. L. Ackoff, "Toward a System of Systems Concepts," to appear in *Management Science* during 1971.

2. *Perception of Reality*

This complex and fundamental element of the action system should, for our purposes, be treated as simply as possible. Such an intention, unfortunately, is not easily carried out for what we called "perception of reality" is the very source of all the experience that underlies, triggers, and motivates action. As we shall presently see, to understand this system element even in a most superficial manner, it will be necessary to introduce a number of its inner dimensions into the discussion. These include such notions as environment, ecology, situation, time, the future, etc., not forgetting their interrelationships. So, as we must start somewhere, let us start with brief descriptions of what we mean by "perception" and by "reality." The rest will enter the argument as the argument is developed.

By *perception* we should understand something more than seeing or observing, and something less than cognition. This in-between ground of consciousness and experience may include: reasoned or accidental insight, associative and analogical thinking, connective memory, the relating of experiences, recognition, assessment, judgment, selection—and, the constant combination and recombination of all the above into new, or rather novel, images and mental constructs.

Reality, that which is perceived, is more elusive. Perhaps an easy way to approach its meaning would be to apply Ortega y Gasset's famous dictum, "I am I, *and* my circumstances," to our Neolithic Hunter. (I choose him, for I see him as being more aware, and living a more multi-dimensional life than his distant ancestor, Early Man.)

Reality, then, is our hunter and his circumstances. Let us say that it is his intellective model of what surrounds him, of what he experiences, and of how he, a conscious human being, relates, reacts and responds to the intricate and interactive dual system of *self* and the self's context.

This dual system is so very complex that even if we reduce the many-fathomed notion of reality to that of environment, we find immediately that man, primitive though he may be, as our hunter is, exists in a number of environments. And these, closely interwoven as they are, remain still sufficiently differentiated to elicit a variety of responses, hence of perceptions.

In calling the hunter "actor," I have been literal in two senses: that of his being the generator of action, and that of his acting in a number of roles. Each role involves a particular context and function, and concomitantly, a different perception of self and the self's surroundings.

In systems discourse, surroundings and context are actually subsumed under the concept "environment," which I shall define as follows:

(2) The environment of a system A (e.g., the hunter) is another system B, a change in any of whose elements can produce a change in the state of system A.

The notion "produce a change" that is contained in the above definition will be understood with greater clarity if we approach the exchange processes that it implies, with reference to the idea of *ecology*. To penetrate this idea we might say that the environment is composed of a multitude of elements which co-exist in a state of dynamic, overall, balance by effecting exchanges whose character is metabolic and whose interactions—viewed in their totality—are systemic. And further, since our hunter is not only an individuated, or discrete, system of action in the environment, but also an element of the environment, he belongs to the exchange process and is part of the general ecology. He is an inextricable part of the ecology not only when he makes tools and uses them, but also when he creates settlements, forms groups, families, societies, institutions, world views, systems of beliefs—in short he belongs to the ecological process in everything he does. This manner of conceiving of ecology greatly enlarges that concept's initial meaning which was restricted to certain biological processes. I believe that such an enlargement of the idea of ecology is absolutely necessary both for planning and for social discourse in general.* Insofar as our hunter is concerned, it should be permissible to argue that making all of his activities a part of the generalized ecological process allows us to see him in true perspective—namely, within a reality that is total, and which totally affects his perception.

But there is still more to this fundamental element "perception of reality." And the *more* is in the interactivity that exists between the two systems: self (man), and self's (man's) many-dimensional environment. This is characterized by relationships which in the language of systems discourse are called "feedback."

We witnessed this latter phenomenon when Early Man picked up that stone, for in doing so he changed (however minutely) his reality. From then on he lived in a different reality, or environment, and though he may not have been conscious of it, that difference affected his perception of all his circumstances. And, in turn, it affected that of his descendants. Early Man's reality and his perception of it changed far more notably with his invention of the sharp edge. Here it becomes evident that, although the feedback pattern may be seen as circular, the interaction of man and environment prevents it from becoming closed. Because of man's creative propensity, exchange between man and the environment is productive of actual change—again, both in man's reality and in his perception of it. And thanks to the feedback and man's creative inputs, the rate of change steadily accelerates. By the time Neolithic Man was making tools, copying them, and innovating, the rate had speeded up greatly—especially if one considers that similar activities and breakthroughs were probably occuring simultaneously in many groups scattered throughout the inhabited world.

* For an elaboration of the necessity of an enlarged definition of ecology, see Hasan Ozbekhan, "Toward a General Theory of Planning," in *Perspectives of Planning*, E. Jantsch, ed., OECD, Paris, 1969.

Then, when human action reached a point where it was able to generate significant change in the environment, man's effort to adapt began to be addressed to man-made events as well as to natural ones.

Over the long perspective of man's interactivity with his environment, we find that, gradually, his adaptive forces have turned away from the once dominant "order" of nature and shifted more and more towards the order of Man. From hunting, he moved to the agricultural mode of life, and later to the industrial, and has now entered the, still somewhat mysterious, "post-industrial" mode. During this evolution the original "disorder in the immediacies" has been largely brought under control, and a totally new environment wherein much immediate disorder of natural origin is *controlled*, represents reality for contemporary man. Consequently, the central problem of man, today, is to adapt himself to a reality that is primarily of his own making.

Since human beings have lived and survived not as single individuals capable only of serial activity, but in groups capable of concerted action, their activity has had a multiplier effect on, and given new dimensions to, the notion of environment. Today, we ought to understand environment as the entire experiential milieu of man, encompassing all things, both abstract and concrete—nature in its multiple aspects, society, institutions, the plethora of artifacts created by man through his technologies, the forms of collective experience we call cultures, ways of life, history, and the accumulated dreams and memories of people.

To try to analyze such a complex and vast system, I once evolved three arbitrary constructs: life/nature centered environment, social/human centered environment, and thing/technology centered environment.[1] The distinctions made by these analytic constructs can be synthesized under the notion of *situation*. By situation we must understand

[1] Hasan Ozbekhan, *Op. Cit.*

not only the state of the environment and of the ecology—
both of which include the consequences of human action—
but a continuum of events that is created by the interactivity of man and environment. Whereas environment and
the state of the ecology or ecological balance suggest certain
static views that have been developed with regard to nature,
situation can be used to represent the real state of the "ecosystem," which is dynamic, hence in continual change, and
whose structure is a *conjuncture* of interlinked events. The
causal patterns of these events are so extraordinarily complex, that we can no longer apprehend them at the level of
empirical observation.

By distinguishing between environment and situation, we
can also speculate that while, in earlier periods, man perceived the environment as a reality that was mainly spatial
in character, more recently, a temporal dimension has been
added. Today, reality is more clearly perceived as a space-
time continuum—another way of saying that the systems
we deal with are "dynamic."

Although we have now come to recognize space and time
as two different modes of conscious perception of reality,
rather than two different entities, something further, and
of vital importance, is implicit in the association of these
two modes of consciousness. It is the idea of the "future"
or "futurity."

For many reasons that, as far as I know, are not wholly
clear, man has tended to articulate his consciousness of time
in terms of *before-and-after*. He has come to perceive reality
by using "references" or "points of reference" that could be
abstracted from a situation at one moment, then compared
with points of reference abstracted from the situation at
another moment. Notable differences represented "change,"
and the interval between the two observations, "time." The
evolution of this convention has made time directional. And
this directionality has become, in itself, a logic—an ordering
agent for events. It is in this sense that E. Huant's remark-

able statement "(that we have) without noticing it, associated the chronological idea with that of causality,"[1] must
be understood.

Once such a logic becomes established, in fact virtually
embedded in the psychological make-up of the human being,
it is normal that he should come initially to view succession
among events as something pre-ordained and, later, as
something causally linked by invariances that are beyond
his power to change or even to influence. Thus, the future
becomes ordered, rigidified along a straight time axis. In
man's mind the image of the future is reduced to a series
of concatenated events, each fitting into a here-and-now
and a there-and-then organized by the idea of before-and
after. It is self-evident that a temporal reality seen and
understood in these terms creates a linearity of vision that
is wholly unsuited for coping with an ever more complex,
ever more proliferating situation. This particular notion of
time and of causality and that it has concomitantly rendered
man incapable of coping with his situation dictated at least
two extremely significant world views: one was "fatalism,"
the other, what we might perhaps call "pragmatism."*

In the view we term fatalistic, events cannot be controlled
by man, because they have their own logic and their own
God-given laws. All man can do, therefore, is to accept events
as they come, and refuse to realize that he contributes by
his acts to the configuration of any situation. Hence, the only
viable relationship that man can have with his surroundings
is to try to adapt to them as best he can, and after the fact.
What this also means is that, because of a particular notion
of causality, man bound by fatalism abdicates the future;

---

[1] *Connaissance du Temps*, Centre d'Etudes Laennec, Lethielleux,
Paris, 1950.

* I am using "pragmatism" in its ordinary meaning and am not
referring to the philosophical system of thought that bears the same
name.

he lives entirely in the present, arguing that the future is beyond the compass of the human mind.

The same notion of causality operates in the view that I have called pragmatic, but somewhat differently. Here, once again, linearity in the conception of time and cause makes man unable to deal with the eventual consequences of his actions. The pragmatist, however, approaches the situation with a deep belief that the immediate, namely, the easily foreseeable, results of his actions constitute the reality he must perceive and cope with. Therefore, what he rejects, or ignores, are future consequences; what he accepts are short-term results. In contradistinction to the fatalist, his attitude is not wholly adaptive, and his responses are not necessarily after the fact. But, like the fatalist, he also abdicates the future, doing so in favor of a small extension of the present.

Although historically, fatalism has been labelled as mainly Eastern and pragmatism as mainly Western, it is rather fascinating to note that in our time they have become melded in technological civilizations. For, though we know that advanced technology owes much to Western pragmatism, it is in the West, now, that we hear statements about the "autonomous dynamics of technology," and about our inborn inability to control it. All of which indicates that fatalism has now become superimposed upon our (the West's) traditionally pragmatic vision of reality.*

These world views and the attitudes resulting from them have had an immense influence on our manner of relating action to the future. They have, in the main, precluded the future from being used as a source of information. They have restricted action to the short-range and directed it almost exclusively toward already known options. They have caused us to ignore or disregard the consequences of our acts by ascribing an overriding primacy to results.

* For a profound exploration of this occurrence, see, J. Ellul, *The Technological Society*, (A. A. Knopf), 1964.

Finally, by insisting on action toward predictable outcomes they have greatly inhibited the organization of planned action systems that are inventive of new concepts and operations—in other words, they have grievously slowed down the growth of a body of knowledge concerned with planning. Another important thing these world views have done was to steer us away (this point is implicit in all the foregoing) from systems of action that have their own elements of disturbance—improbability—built into them. This might be one of the chief reasons why we have been so successful in technological endeavors and so inept in creating flexible and evolutionary social institutions.

All these points will reappear in one form or another as our argument advances. Nevertheless, I felt that they needed to be touched upon here under the heading of "perception of reality" for they provide a useful, or at least a suggestive, background for the following definitions:

(3) Perception of reality refers to a human agent's experience of his self in relation to the situation which is the self's context.

(4) Perception of reality is the fundamental element of a human action system, inasmuch as human action occurs in response to the environmental, ecological, and temporal events and processes that become interlinked in situation.

(5) Perception of reality changes in response to human action because situation changes as a result of human action.

3. *Ends*

I shall begin by defining the element "end(s)" in a somewhat unusual way, by emphasizing its value connotations.

(6) End(s) refers to a particular conception of the value content, or requiredness, of any action's outcome and consequences.

What this definition attempts to underscore is the fact

that any line of action is undertaken, always, after a value judgment has been made concerning either the immediate results and/or the farther impacts that will follow from it.

At the most fundamental level of value discourse such judgments are embodied in the twin ideas of "good" and "bad." What falls into each of these categories proliferates as the situation alters and perception of reality, thereby, changes. For instance, we assumed that Early Man had a single end which embraced all aspects of "the good"— namely, *survival* as a biological entity. The notion of survival can be generalized (even in the above case) by saying that from man's point of view any action which tilts the metabolic rate of exchange between environment and man in man's favor, is good. If the picking up of the stone and the eventual invention of the sharp edge helped man achieve a somewhat more favorable rate of exchange, then "the good" inhered to the stone and the sharp edge, as well as to the actions that led to the picking up of the first and the invention of the second.

When we reach the Neolithic Hunter we find that ends have multiplied and so have values expressing "the good." Many social and technological innovations have occurred that help man weight the balance a bit more advantageously. The initial family has evolved into a more complex and effective social grouping: the tribe. Knowledge regarding the relatively orderly government of such tribes has developed, and so has technological knowledge. Tools are more specialized, functionally differentiated and therefore, more efficient. All these gains can be put into the category of "the good." As such they represent ends that must be repeatedly and continuously striven for.

Although it is not my intention here to dwell at any length on negative factors corresponding to the notion of "the bad," it should be noted that the proliferation of human action and its success in creating a reality that is more man-made than natural, has had very grave long-range consequences whose correction may well represent the current basic task of planned action. One of the most blatant consequences of the dominance of man over nature has been the profound disruption of our ecological balance. The effects of this disruption are already being sensed, but its ultimate impacts as yet are far from clear. Accustomed to "conquering" or "subduing" nature, man seems to have forgotten that he is an intrinsic part of that very nature, and in the long run this lapse in memory may undermine or destroy his ability to survive. What I earlier called disorder in the immediacies, and by which I meant a particular perception of the human situation, has now become a disorder that is almost wholly the result of human action. The necessity for coping with this kind of disorder has given tremendous impetus to, and had a major effect on, the idea of planning.

To return to the notion of ends: it is a rich one. It possesses a wealth of meaning and dimensions—one being the aforementioned proliferating interpretations that "the good" accumulates in the course of history. Beginning with "survival," things like food, tools, shelter, body cover, etc., come to objectify value. Later, less tangible inventions are imbued with value: the tribe, society, various institutions, the economy, the law—such lists can be extended almost *ad infinitum*. At a still higher level, and under far more evolved conditions, systems of thought and ideas, beliefs, commitments, religions, the self, justice, equality, respect, dignity, knowledge, plenty, beauty, and similar notions enter into the discourse.

What is the meaning of this proliferation within the value-space of individuals and societies? It is, that as situations become more complex, the single initial value of survival recedes into the background; it becomes a universal given, and is screened from direct view by a multitude of hierarchically ordered norms that organize and direct human action. Consequently, "the good" (except in its strictly ethical sense) becomes by degrees translated into "the desirable." In turn, ends come to define conceptions of the *desirable outcomes* or consequences of a system of action. And values that inhere to such conceptions are utilized as *criteria* for *preference* or *choice,* or as *justifications for planned or actual action.**

To see values in this light makes it possible to say that ends specify an action's *anticipatory* basis. They do so by defining and justifying the boundaries, or the field, of outcomes that *ought,* and by implication *can,* be preferred and chosen.

The process which underlies the above interpretation has been explicated by E. G. Mesthene, as follows:

> "It seems clear that values in this sense [referring to Robin Williams' interpretation] have their origins in the pattern of choice behavior that are characteristic of any given society. What we mean when we say that a society is committed to certain values is that the people in that society will typically make judgments and choose to act in ways that reveal and reinforce those values. It seems equally clear that choice behavior is determined, or at least circumscribed, by the options available to choose from at the time the choice is made."[1]

Concerning ends we can now make the following points, especially with reference to planning: (i) in order for man to act (rationally), a near or distant outcome must be visualized; (ii) such an outcome must be desirable; (iii) the desirability of an outcome can be judged in terms of its value, and the action leading to this outcome justified in terms of such value; (iv) if the actor has to choose among several outcomes, his preference for one particular outcome must also be justified with respect to its value; (v) choice

---

* I have based this analysis, almost by paraphrasing, on Robin Williams' definition of value which is quoted in E. G. Mesthene, *Technological Change,* Harvard University Press, Cambridge, Mass. 1970.

[1] *Op. Cit.*

among outcomes enters into the action equation only when there are alternative valued outcomes available to the actor; (vi) the spectrum of alternative valued outcomes corresponds to the spectrum of options open to the actor.*

4. *Knowledge*

Knowledge is what we might call a *generalized* element of the action system because it pervades and suffuses all the other elements. Thus, "perception of reality" is a kind of knowledge—at least, it is at its source, in the form of experience. Similarly, it is possible to say that because ends, purposes, objectives, means, and goals can be known, they are also part of an actor's knowledge. Nevertheless, our own purposes dictate that rather than probing into the knowledge component of every element we should try to understand three points in some detail; these being: knowledge *per se,* knowledge about ends, and knowledge about means. If we succeed in doing this we shall avoid repetition, for all the other elements can, insofar as their knowledge content is concerned, be subsumed explicitly or implicitly, under what we will be saying.

With regard to knowledge *per se,* I shall limit myself to quoting from an article by Paul Weiss in which he showed how knowledge comes into being not through accretion but by assimilation. Thus, knowledge grows:

> ". . . beginning from its source—experience, still unprocessed. Probing of the environment furnishes raw data of information, which are either stored as records for future use of analysed forthwith. The products of

---

* E.g., until the invention of the sharp edge, Early Man had very limited options with regard to the stone: pounding, hitting, throwing. After the sharp edge was invented future potentialities increased, but except for cutting, the available options did not. The Neolithic Hunter, on the other hand, could choose among various options; he could make axes, arrowheads, lance tips, picks, etc. As the value content of each of these can be assumed to have been equal, the justification of his preference for the axe head was most likely governed by considerations that we shall discuss under the heading of "Objectives."

analysis are then screened and sorted according to relevance. Irrelevant ones go into discard, sharing the fate of records become obsolete. And from this sorting, the pile of data emerges as an ordered system, catalogued and classified, yet each item revealing its erstwhile identity . . .

"In various stages of evaluation, such packaged information is then widely circulated, leading to confluence and critical correlation with countless correlations from other sources. From this synthetic process, hypotheses emerge, which, upon further verification, turn into integral parts of the body of knowledge—theorems, principles, rules, and laws—general formulas which not only supersede the itemized accounts from which they were derived, but can dispense with the further search for items of information, which they predictively subsume.

"At this stage, data have become assimilated, have lost their individual identities in merging with that higher identity—the body of organized knowledge. A patchwork of unrelated facts that has become transformed into a rationally connected thought structure of inner consistency, viable and durable, subject to the test of survival and the adaptive improvements of evolution . . ."[1]

This analysis of knowledge as a "growth process" is sufficient to explicate the manner in which knowledge *per se* becomes embodied into the human action system. Now let us explore how knowledge about ends and knowledge about means enters into the framework we have established.

a. *Knowledge about Ends*

We will start by proposing that:

(7) Knowledge concerning ends is widely assimilated and operationalized information about the value content of the outcomes and of the consequences of particular actions.

---

[1]"Knowledge: a Growth Process," *Science*, June 10, 1960, Vol. 131, No. 3415, pp. 1716-1719.

What this says is that knowledge of ends is that body of experience that has been analysed, sorted, ordered, diffused, correlated, accepted—in short organized and assimilated in the form of general principles whose function is to define the outcomes and the consequences of an action as either "good" or "bad."

The highly important point that needs to be made with reference to the above is that the value content of what we have called an *outcome* is relatively easy to determine in the light of experience, whereas the value content of a distant *consequence* cannot be determined in the same manner. This point can be illustrated by means of our examples.

We have described the world of our first actor Early Man as one wherein a single primary value—survival—defined the ends of action. In such a world any thing that helped tilt the exchange processes between man and the environment in man's favor was a good; hence, the sharp edge once invented could immediately be imbued with value. From that point on, all the applications of the sharp edge were outcomes possessing the attribute of goodness and desirability. Furthermore, this attribute was strengthened by what we might refer to as "slow time," meaning by this expression that the eventual consequences of sharp edged tools which we can generalize into the eventual ecological consequences of technology, were too remote to be either relevant or imaginable.

Later, in the case of our Neolithic Hunter, we have seen that copying activity tended to accelerate time, mainly by speeding up the action system. This tendency has continued through mechanization and automation, so that today we find ourselves in a situation whose characteristic is very rapid change. This important fact has had the effect of compressing the lengthy distances that used to exist between outcomes and consequences. Yet, in the interim, we did not develop the attitudes and the states of mind that would allow us to gain the kind of knowledge which might enable us to make value judgments concerning consequences, namely to assess the impacts (the further impacts) of the outcomes we know how to achieve. Both our vision and our moral sensitivity have remained rivetted to outcomes, that is, to immediate results.

There are many reasons for this state of affairs and we have touched upon some of them. However, there is one event of great importance that we have not had an opportunity to mention up to now: it is the emergence, from Neolithic times onward, of a specific value that we call "utility."

I think that it would be correct to say that the concept of utility arose and became preponderant in human consciousness, when the goodness, hence the desirability, of tools began to be taken for granted—and this occurred when copying them grew relatively easy. It is beneath this trend that we discern an occurrence of vast and lasting import: a massive shift in valuation patterns from the multiple ends that action is directed toward, to rather restricted outcomes the majority of which consisted of *things* that are useful. It is, therefore, to this shift that we must ascribe the early emergence and continuing dominance of utility as a general value. It is also to this shift that we must ascribe our traditional obsession with the short-range, the immediate, the immediately useful outcome, as well as our continuing neglect of the outcome's longer and larger consequences.

This attitude—by now an almost inborn psychological human trait—has had another effect worthy of note. It was the increasing preference that was, and continues to be, given to the development of knowledge concerning means. The point to be remembered with respect to this latter aspect of our psycho-social evolution is that knowledge about means, and valuation of utility for its own sake, does not inform us (quite to the contrary) of the long-term consequences of our actions, although our present situation is giving us rather clear warning that overemphasis on utility embodied in things is destroying our ecosytem. This indicates to us that, for planning, the importance we ascribe to ends *per se,* and the knowledge we must develop about consequences, is critical.

b. *Knowledge about Means*

We have subsumed two elements of our action system: "rules" and "skills" under means, and will give a general definition of knowledge in relation to these two concepts.

(8) Knowledge pertaining to means is information about the rules that optimize the effectiveness of any action and maximize efficiency in the application of any skill.

What, then, do we mean by *rule?*

(9) Rules are general principles that define and dictate the procedures of any action whose ends and goals are given.*

The notion of rules is both important and somewhat confused. Rules are criterial elements, and this makes them very akin to values. They differ, however, from values in that they do not derive from the notion of "good," but from that of "right." Rules are *norms* which stipulate the manner in which something must be done. They form the theoretical background for customs, laws, regulations, skills, etc. They underlie every act about which we can say that there is a right and wrong way to go about it.

"Right" in English, as well as in most Western European languages, is an adjective with a long and continuous history. And although it is now burdened (or enriched) by a wide variety of connotations, it is striking to note how little these deviate from its original meaning.

In one form or another the notion of "right" corresponds to that of "rule" and to "what is conformable to the rule,

---

* It should be evident from this definition that I am subsuming under the concept "rule," the theorems, principles, laws, general formulas, etc. which are mentioned in the above quotation from Paul Weiss with reference to knowledge.

whether the rule be physical or mental . . . a right line, a right conclusion, a right action."[1] At several levels of discourse we find the correspondence between "right" and "rule" is direct and constant. A straight line is called "right", because the drawing of it is controlled by the geometrical instrument which was formerly called "rule", and only rather recently, "ruler." Similarly, any key is right for a given lock when it obeys the rules governing the relations between lock form and key form.

Thus it is necessary to distinguish between *rule*, which is a norm, and *utility*, which is a value. The distinction can be made as follows: (i) a thing is right, or the opposite, in relation to the rule that governs it; (ii) a thing is useful, or the opposite, in relation to the result it aims to achieve. Implicit in this distinction is a very important notion: the "predictability" of an action's outcome, and of the outcome's consequences.

If an action system is governed by verified rules, the outcome of the action is predictable. However, if an action system is governed by values alone, its outcome is not predictable. In other words, there are types of action whose norms are clearly established and form part of our general knowledge. The Neolithic Hunter *knows* that if he chips a piece of sylex in "certain ways," the outcome will be an axe head; if he chips it in "other ways," the outcome will be an arrowhead, etc. Those "certain" and "other" *ways* of chipping are different rules that make him able to predict one outcome as against another. Therefore, this type of action (the making of things) is possessed, even at this early stage, of rules—conformance to which guarantees the obtaining of the desired outcome. Thus, information is bunched at the beginning of the process.

Now, if we take the action pattern of Early Man, we find that it is not at all the same. He picks up a rock, for the first time, being motivated solely by the end: survival. But

[1] F. H. Bradley, *Ethical Studies*, Oxford, 1876.

he doesn't *know,* that first time, that the rock actually will help him survive better—that it will be *useful* to him. For him, the information is clustered at the end of the process. He cannot predict; he has to *learn.*

Let us look for a moment at what happens during the time span between Early Man and his Neolithic descendant. The value motivation to act, slowly crystallizes around what we might call a "norm-motivation." The end, survival, becomes virtually identified with the necessity to know certain rules that will insure expected outcomes. If we express this change in planning terms, we should say that the rules (for making things) were, in fact, shifting information from the area of improbability, which is the future, towards the present—the overall tendency being to bunch the information at the beginning of the action process.

This shift (outlined in Figure 8) represents the fundamental effort of what I shall soon call "orthodox planning," in which it takes the form of forecasting.

In connection with this tendency, the significant question we must now raise is: Does the shift change anything? The answer is: Yes, in the type of action we are analyzing, i.e. technological action, it does; but it does so only insofar as outcomes are concerned. That which lies beyond the outcome, that which we have called "consequences," remains unpredictable. Were we, here, to speed up our argument faster than is warranted, and ask: Why? The answer would probably be that we have developed no rules for such predictions although it has been the aim of planning as an intellectual discipline to do so. Whether such an aim is either legitimate or feasible is something that we shall have to determine later. Meanwhile let us turn to the second aspect of means, "skills:"

(10) Skills refer to the physical or intellectual dexterity that a person is able to apply so as to bring about a specific desired outcome in terms of rules that pertain to the attainment of such an outcome.

From a purely operational standpoint, skill is the bringing about of a specific outcome when the necessary conditions for its attainment are present—a major condition being knowledge pertinent to a particular action. Given this knowledge and sufficient aptitude on the part of the individual, skills may be acquired with comparative ease. Thus, skills always represent the individualized level of the action system, and their existence is determined exclusively with reference to the person who is acting.

Skill is primarily measured in terms of "efficiency," and this, in large part, is dependent on the degree to which a particular action has been explored, evolved and, in some sense, automatized. Once our hunter knows how to make an axe, it becomes permissible to surmise that the more axes he makes the better he will make them. Increased efficiency may be manifest either in time gained or in incremental improvements in the object's design.

From these cursory considerations we can say:

a. Skills are predicated on pre-existing knowledge of the functional characteristics of the objects acted upon.

b. Skills can be acquired by learning the rules that govern them, that is empirically, without reference to the abstract elements of the action system.

c. Skills, consequently, operate most efficiently when the outcome is a "copy" of something; they do not seem to form part of the action system insofar as creative action is concerned.

These few points shed an interesting light on the historical evolution of the element, skill, in human action systems. As the need for more and more copies increased and demands for maximized efficiency became imperative, the impetus to make skills mechanical accelerated, and reached its apogee in the industrial era. These trends can be found both with regard to skills at the conceptual level and those

at the operational. Curiously enough, the whole evolution
skills from the human action system. Therefore, methods
can be interpreted as a centuries-long attempt to *disconnect*
and techniques have been conceived and developed which
tend to act as "algorithms" that are capable of solving
applications' problems automatically, mnemonically and
repetitively. The propensity has been to translate skills into
rules and mechanisms that operate by themselves. Thus on
the applied, or operational level, skills have become embodied
in the tools themselves—first in the machine, then the computer, which latter recognized the skill concept in an
intermediate area of memory simulation and mechanical
control of operations.

These tendencies should be kept in mind for they will
bear on our discussion of planning. We must also remember,
as we leave "skill" and go on to "purpose," that the human
being realized quite early that his inborn skills were extremely limited, and that inventions compensating for this
limitation had to be made.

5. *Purpose*

Purpose is generally considered as the fundamental teleological element of an action system, (the other such elements being ends, objectives and goals). However, its fate
in the history of ideas has been the same as that which befell
teleology; it was discarded because of the difficulties that
attempts to explain the processes of causality raised. This
attitude of rejection and even of outright condemnation is
now being reconsidered, mainly thanks to the efforts of
systems scientists and some theoreticians of planning. The
newly emergent view is well illustrated in the following
statement:

> "Since we consider purposefulness a concept necessary
> for the understanding of certain modes of behavior
> we suggest that a teleological study is useful if it avoids

problems of causality and concerns itself merely with an investigation of purpose."[1]

I am not sure that in the study of action systems it is actually possible to avoid "problems of causality" altogether, but I am certain that the notion of purpose has to be re-introduced into the discourse.

Purpose can be defined simply enough:

(11) Purpose is the intention to act.

Yet, the very simplicity of the definition makes the concept extremely hard to interpret or explore, because the idea of "intention" is complex and often ambiguous. In trying to come to grips with it, one recognizes that the intention to do something (anything) does not spring up in the mind out of nothing; obviously, then, neither can purpose. To become crystallized, intention must be triggered. The question is: What triggers it?

Prima facie, we know that a person's perception of reality, that is, of his situation, creates a number of responses capable of taking shape as intentions. We also know that any such intention must, if it is to lead to directed action, be informed by knowledge of ends as well as of means. When such knowledge is available then the action system can operate in the manner of purposeful systems. This type of system is defined by R. L. Ackoff as:

(12) "A purposeful system is one which can produce the same outcome in different ways in the same (internal or external) state, and can produce different outcomes in the same or different states."[1]

This means that a system that is purposeful can, under conditions that are relatively constant, make selections with

---

[1] A. Rosenblueth, N. Wiener, J. Bigelow, "Behavior, Purpose and Teleology," in *Modern Systems Research for the Behavioral Scientist*, W. Buckley, ed. Aldine Publishing Co., Chicago, 1968.

[1] *Op. Cit.*

regard to outcomes, ends and means. Selecting involves what we generally call "will," and in purposeful systems the triggering mechanism of action is *will*.

Will comes into consciousness from many sources, both external and internal to the individual. The intensity of its manifestation obviously varies according to the individual's character structure and his perception. Nevertheless, we can circumscribe the notion of will, because we know that the boundaries within which a thing can be willed are delineated by values. We also know that values become articulated as ends when they are (i) permissible, being expressions of "the good;" and (ii) feasible, being so defined by available knowledge about means.

Therefore, purpose, or the intention of doing something, or better, the will to action, involves the meshing of judgment and assessment. To put it differently, purpose operates as an internal information exchange and feed-back process that guides action and controls it, both with reference to ends and to all the other elements that compose the action system.

In planned action the "control" aspect of purpose becomes the most important, and involves not only control pure and simple, but "control and coordination."

The problem now arises: given the outcome(s) we have chosen in the light of clearly defined ends and available means, does the action system as a whole lead us to the outcome(s)? This problem, incidentally, is a continuous one for, today, the situation in terms of which outcome(s) are chosen is highly dynamic and changing. Hence, for planning as an action system to lead us to the outcome(s) we have chosen, continuous adjustment (control and coordination) of the system to the changing situation is an absolute necessity. At times this may dictate that the action pattern (not the system) be changed, i.e. new, adaptive, short-term "decisions" be made with regard to the organization of the action. In other instances, it may require that the chosen outcomes be changed by making longer-term decisions. All these changes are controlled and coordinated by purpose.

Clearly, the way purpose operates has a profound effect on the "choice-behavior" of the action system as a whole. This point should become clearer as we explore the notion of an "objective–goal nexus."

6. *The Objective/Goal Nexus*

To understand the important action elements that objective(s) and goal(s) comprise, we shall have to return to where we began our line of thinking and briefly review certain aspects of its development. In our initial model of action (Figure 1) neither objectives nor goals appear for the obvious reason that Early Man, when he first picks up a rock, has none as far as we know. In the next stage (Figure 2), the sharp edge has been invented. Nevertheless, objectives remain implicit, whereas the "goal" has emerged as a conscious element. It is not until the subsequent general model (Figure 3) that objectives enter the action system as a discrete element—an element belonging, along with purpose and goal, to the "option evaluation and decision" field. Why did objectives remain confused with ends in our model of creative action (Figure 2) while goal did not?

With respect to goal the answer is obvious. Once the sharp edge has been discovered, this invention becomes something desirable in the light of the end (survival) to be served. And from this point on, the picking up of rocks is done with a definite *preferred outcome* in view, i.e. that of making them sharp. The means may not have been refined, but sharpening exists and so we can assume that, one way or another, it occurs directly after rocks are picked up, and that rocks are picked up to be sharpened. What still remains undefined is the fan of all the possible applications of this invention—the potentialities to be worked out over time—that is, until people become aware of these potentialities or latent options. Since awareness of the existence of options is a condition (though not the sole one) for the setting of objectives, it is clear that objectives could not be articulated at the stage of original creative action.

When our Neolithic Hunter arrives on the scene, there is definite awareness of options. Functionally differentiated objects: "lance tip," "pick," "axe," "arrowhead," etc. have become concrete alternative applications of the sharp edge. Moreover there is knowledge of the means (rules and skill) for making them, and the ends for which they will be made are defined and valued.

The Neolithic Hunter, as he picks up a rock that early evening, evaluates and makes a choice. We can imagine him thinking: "Here is a rock. It is sylex. (We watched him hesitate to make sure of this.) Therefore, it is hard, and can be chipped (transformed) easily into a tool. Out of it I can make a lance tip or a pick, an axe head or an arrowhead or something else that I and my group value."

At this point he may stop thinking, pick up the rock and go on. He has ascertained certain outcomes the rock can be made to serve, confirmed his ability to change the rock into something useful, and has acted purposefully in picking up the rock. All this he will have done, but without having set a precise objective or goal.

On the other hand he might continue his reasoning. Let's imagine that he does. "I have two lances already," he thinks, "and enough arrowheads. I don't need a pick—my lance tips serve almost the same ends. And anyway this piece of sylex is large and heavy; it would be a waste to break it up. It is almost triangular too, therefore it is ideally suited for making an axe head. My own axe head is old; I've sharpened it so often there's not much of it left. Soon it will be of little use to me for cutting the wood we shall need now that the cold season is coming. The only thing I can still do with it is to turn it into a pounding tool (hammer), and replace it with the axe I shall make out of this piece of sylex

I have found." After having reasoned in this fashion, we see him pick up the sylex and disappear into the forest.

In the course of such reasoning, the Neolithic Hunter has not only assured himself of the ends to be served (and thereby, made value judgments) ; but he has evaluated the alternative options that are available to him, in the light of his situation. He has made a choice which to him appears optimal, given the information he has relative to that situation. And in making his choice he has now set himself a clear and discrete objective, as well as a clear and specific goal.

What is that objective? It is to cut wood in order to prepare for the oncoming winter. And the objective is formulated after other options of equal or similar value have been considered, weighed and discarded. What is the goal? It is to make the axe in order to be able to attain his objective. It is evident that both cutting the wood and making the axe are preferred outcomes chosen from among a number of other desirable outcomes. What, then, is the difference between objective and goal? The following definition will answer this question:

(13) "The objective of a purposeful system in a particular situation is a preferred outcome that cannot be obtained within a specified period but which can be obtained over a longer time period."[1]

(14) "The goal of a purposeful system in a particular situation is a preferred outcome that can be obtained within a specified time period."[2]

Thus in systems terminology, objectives as well as goals refer to *preferred outcomes* whose attainment is governed by different time horizons. This distinction, however, is sometimes mistakenly interpreted, and the mistake consists in the fact that the distant "outcome" embodied in objective

[1] R. L. Ackoff, *Op. Cit.*

[2] Ibid.

is viewed as an abstract idea, while the closer "outcome" represented by goal is taken to be an already concrete fact. This, of course, is not the case. A goal is as much an abstract conceptualization of an outcome, as an objective is. The concrete outcome is produced, not as a result of setting a goal, but as a result of acting in the light of a goal. The decision to make an axe does not, of itself, produce the axe. The concretization of the idea into the object that the idea defines, depends on many things: e.g., skills in effecting the required transformation, or, the way in which a person meets the demands of competing objectives and goals that the many roles he plays within his social or situational setting impose upon him, etc.

One centrally important thing happens with the setting of a goal, however. The action system becomes directed. Thus we can no longer say that our hunter will make an axe or something else. Insofar as we know, he will make an axe. If he changes his mind, then a new choice and decision cycle will have to be gone through. If he keeps to his decision, the translation from objective to goal will have narrowed down and focused his action pattern upon a preferred outcome, toward which he can, and must, now act.

Figure 4 is an attempt to describe this process diagrammatically. This figure is also a somewhat detailed reconceptualization of the general conclusions we have so far reached. The action system is viewed in temporal terms: present and future; while the situation is conceived as encompassing, interactively, the elements: perception of reality, ends, knowledge, and purpose/will. A preliminary set of options has shifted into the present, and it is indicated that both imaginable objectives and available means can operate upon these options. The system, thus described, is therefore purposeful and subject to choice behavior. The goal is located in the option-space where it defines the immediate preferred outcome (axe) dictated by the objective of cutting wood which, itself, is a component of a future option-space. If the action system is looked at as a whole, it is now possible to see that the consequence of making an axe will (can) be the cutting of wood. And we can translate this into the statement that the objective has dictated the goal, or that a future consequence has dictated present action. This is already a rather extraordinary step. It implies that the action system has become "anticipatory," and that the anticipation is "causative" of choice, and of action. The import of this for planning and planned action is almost self-evident, especially if we note that the old feed-back loops going from the present *and* future option spaces into the present—thereby changing both knowledge and perception of reality—continue to operate. Their operation bounds the system, so to speak. And as the whole cluster of elements in the situation continues to affect objectives and means, we begin to be confronted with increasing change.

Another way of visualizing this process, but only in terms of a concatenation of objectives and goals, will be found in Figure 5.

This schema merely indicates that when one gazes at a far distant time horizon, one realizes that any current goal (or goals) has been derived from sets of objectives that yielded new goals, which yielded other sets of objectives, that led to still other goals, and so on. Time, it would appear, enters into planned action in a way that may be very different from what we have hitherto observed.

7. *The Act/Consequence Nexus*

In Figure 4 "act" and "consequence" are interlinked. The overlap space should be understood as representing "outcome," and the relationships between these three notions made clear for, otherwise, they may cause confusion.

(15) "An act of a system is a system event for the occurrence of which no change in the system's environment is either necessary or sufficient."[1]

---

[1] R. L. Ackoff, *Op. Cit.*

This definition says that given a goal which conceptually describes a preferred immediate outcome, and objectives that describe a preferred long-term outcome(s), and means that render the attainment of the goal possible and that of the objective conceivable, the act of attaining the goal—the actual making of the axe head—is a system element which, of itself can be seen as something independent of any further new occurrences in the environment. Therefore, the immediate outcome embodied in the goal as idea can now be reached as a result of the action system's internal behavior. Thus insofar as we are concerned we can proceed from the assumption that once we have gone through the entire decision process, as we have done, the expected and preferred outcome will result from the act. The only point we need remember is that there is a specifiable time interval which defines the length of the act. E.g., the making of an axe will take less time than, say, the building of a hut. This time interval could be seen as the act's "duration." It is very different from the time interval that divides outcome and consequence, namely, the present and the future.

It is this temporal distinction that leads us to place consequence outside the action system.

(16) A consequence is a future (i.e., temporally distant) impact of any act or outcome upon the environment, which changes the environment in ways that are significant enough to create a new situation.

What should be especially noted with reference to consequence is the strong feedback that it eventually redirects into the fundamental action element we have called "perception of reality." The meaning of this is both simple and clear: human action, taken cumulatively and in its generality, alters the environment in the long run. The axe will fell trees, kill animals and people, help construct other tools, shelters, etc. We know that change in the environment affects perception of reality, that where there is constant creative or innovative input from man into the environment we have a dynamic situation of accelerating change, and that in time the content of the action system (values embodied in ends, dimensions of knowledge, rules and skills pertaining to means, purpose, objectives and goals) will change although the structure of the model remains the same. The phasing of this dynamic, iterative and interactive process is illustrated in Figure 6.

III. THE IDEA OF PLANNING

A. Change and the Contemporary Situation

In the foregoing analysis of the human action system we have repeatedly said that *change* is an intrinsic consequence of action, and that it occurs both in the environment and in man's perception of reality. Some other points we made regarding change were: that its effects are cumulative over time; that it tends to multiply and accelerate; that it inheres more and more to man-made events, and less and less to natural events; that because of this peculiar dynamic the very notion of survival had altered, evolving gradually from a preoccupation with the disorder of nature, to a preoccupation with disorders that result from human activity. It is toward this latter point that we shall henceforth direct our attention.

In the examples we chose we purposely looked at a world that was virtually empty of human beings, and we tried to speculate on the structure of action, hoping as we did this, to understand a number of its characteristics such as creativity, accumulation of knowledge and skills, and the dynamic relationships that slowly gave the action system its teleological—that is, purpose-motivated and future-directed—dimensions. We also tried to show how the individual began to control his action in ways that would serve his fundamental value, survival, more and more efficiently. This progression of the action pattern led us to think—at least by implication—that the various component elements of the action system came to be knitted together by something we would, nowadays, call "rationality." At least, we watched individual rationality emerge amid the changes that individual action generated; and we saw those changes become incorporated into an ever-complexifying situation. However, only briefly did we touch upon the crucial fact that, in time, the cumulative consequences of action resulting in cumulative change would create a situation which could no longer be ordered by individual action alone, nor, for that matter, by individual rationality; namely, by single human beings, or by groups of them, seeking to reach their own ends in conformance with rational rules of action they had inherited from the past. To understand this point, let us leave the dawn of human history and place ourselves in the context of contemporary reality. What do we see?

To begin with we find that our planet is no longer a sparsely inhabited place. Quite the contrary, we see that in some parts it is crowded, in others overcrowded. We see that both creativity and innovation have fairly well conquered and subdued nature; certainly, they have changed it almost beyond recognition. The world of our Neolithic Hunter (we need no longer bother with Early Man) was first altered, profoundly, by an invention called "agriculture." And now in some technologically advanced countries we find that agriculture has been replaced by another invention called "industry." We note that these fundamental changes, affecting both the configuration of the environment and the configuration of human outlook and perception, have had incalculable impacts on our values, our purposes, our objectives and goals, and that these impacts have had even greater effect in the area of our means. This has come about because the majority of important changes sprang from the concentrated effort that man, in general, made to improve the means or techniques which extend human action and, thereby, make it more effective and efficient in the age-old struggle with nature.

The picture I am sketching is an overall one, and although one could refine it by saying that it does not apply in every respect to the whole of our planet, it still portrays our general reality with sufficient accuracy to obviate the need of burdening the argument by the elaboration of details.

The principal point I want to make is that, as our earlier analysis indicated it would, our reality has changed multi-dimensionally; and it has done so as a consequence of cumulative human action that was based on various evolutionary forms of individual rationality.

Now, the question to be asked is: What of it! What does this generally known fact teach us?

To answer the question meaningfully, I must go back to the first paragraph of this section and remind myself, as well as the reader, that our situation today is one in which our earlier preoccupation with survival in the midst of natural events has been succeeded by an increasingly anxious preoccupation with survival amid man-made events. Once this critical fact is imprinted on our minds, we can go on to wonder whether individual rationality that, from Neolithic times on has structured and guided individual action, should not, itself, be put to question in a situation which has become as precarious as ours now is?

When we say we must now survive amid man-made events, we are simply saying that the nature of the disorder in the immediacies has changed, but that disorder continues to exist, indeed has even been aggravated, and it is generated by our own actions—the actions of individuals acting *as* individuals, whether singly or in groups, in the light of inherited patterns of individual rationality. If this fact be true, then the ordering of our present disorder calls for a reorganization of our action patterns at a higher level than that of the individual. This, in turns, calls for a rationality that transcends the individual and becomes embodied in something else.

It will be noted that I have not said "becomes embodied in society." I did not, for in the contemporary world individuated societies of various kinds and bearing various labels exist, but all of them, regardless of the names they bear (including "collective"), are basically individualistic in that their rationalities which are embedded in their traditions, institutions, culture, etc., operate in ways that are fragmented. Hence they, too, act virtually in the same way that single human beings act; namely, with reference to values, purposes, objectives and goals that reflect their limited interests. This fragmentation contributes to the disorder of our situation just as much as individual persons do—and indicates that our evolution has perhaps passed the "social" stage, and that order must be sought at a higher, global, level.

We may be able to illustrate the points I have just tried to make if we think of humanity as a whole in terms of a gaseous mass whose component atoms or particles, viewed either singly or in clusters, are rational and behave rationally, whereas the gaseous mass, itself, is wholly innocent of any rationality whatsoever. Therefore, the next evolutionary step that we must try to envision is the infusion of rational behavior into the *whole* system. This is the same as saying that the rationality of the *parts* must be reorganized at the level of the whole.

How can this be done? There is no clear answer, and no generally agreed upon approach. But it seems, to me at least, that in certain emergent conceptions of planning a number of new and pregnant ideas might be found—especially if we bear firmly in mind that by planning we should understand a particular manner of organizing human action at a higher level of discourse.

B. Roots and Perspectives of Planning

What we call "planning" is the anticipatory decision continuum that enters into any rational human action system, and interlinks all the system elements by directing them toward preferred outcomes.

This manner of viewing planning indicates that, in one way or another, it is always present in human action as the action system's overall organizing component. However, it should be added immediately that until relatively recently, planning has played an implicit rather than an explicit role in our studies of human behavior and of decision making processes. It is only in the course of the past decade or so that serious and more or less systematic attention has been given to the exploration of planning *per se*. Hence, our knowledge of it remains, at best, fragmentary, not to say incomplete and inadequate. This neglect may be one of the factors that are responsible for the perpetuation, as well as the reinforcement, of certain traditional action patterns and intellectual outlooks, which are proving wholly insufficient to deal with our contemporary situation.

From the viewpoint of its historical evolution, I believe that one can correctly see planning as a constant attempt to shift information from the future to the present. It is this tendency which is at the source of all our ideas concerning planning and of most subsequent formal descriptions of it. Therefore, it might be worthwhile to look at some of the assumptions underlying this very old and general approach to planned action. Such assumptions can be grouped under three headings each of which describes a particular evolutionary phase of the idea of planning. These are: (i) planning from the past; (ii) extrapolative planning; and, (iii) planning through forecasting.

The first mode is predicated on the implicit assumption that human action produces virtually no change, and that, therefore, it is feasible to derive references that describe the present from experience, from the past. Planning from past reference points amounts to no more than ordering the present in the image of what has been. It is, if we make a play on words, an exercise for "anticipating the present." It attempts to insure that the same events will be repeated, and the same consequences will ensue from action. Obviously, one can only attain this type of equilibrium by confining oneself almost entirely to repetitive action. But since any cumulative action changes the environment in some way or other, it is evident that this manner of planning severely inhibits the adaptive capabilities of those who use it. Hence, another way had to be found, and was. That it, too, proved to be a dead-end is beside the point, for it has had an immense impact on human vision and behavior in general, and is still with us to a quite considerable extent.

This new way, which I have called "extrapolative planning," also represents a decision process which tries to bring the information concerning a future outcome into the present and, thereby, reduce uncertainty. This second major mode of planning does not seek to extend the past into the present, but rather extend the present into the future. It does so by hypothesizing that the future will be the same as the present, and by acting in such a manner as to make it so. The general idea is graphically depicted in Figure 7. Our main criticism of this mode is similar to that regarding the first; once again, change is almost completely ignored. Consequently, in the long run, human action continually alters the situation and makes it impossible ever to integrate the situation with the kind of planning process that linear extrapolation stands for. Plan and situation remain disparate because "reality" is perceived as a highly stable continuation of the present state of the system, and change regarded as occurring at sufficiently lengthy intervals and in dimensions so minor, that adaptation after the fact is not considered a problem.

Such an assumption is patently false, but it has guided

human action in a large number of societies, which are now viewed as primitive, and also guided it in many modern corporations, most of which have become defunct.

The next evolutionary stage, planning through forecasting as sketched in Figure 8, is also deterministic. Although still very elementary, this type of planning is so widely applied, even now, that it can be termed "orthodox planning." It is grounded on various assumptions such as:

    a. that the present situation has a dynamic that will dictate the content of its own future state in a given time-interval;

    b. that this future state can be forecast and, thereby, become part of the information base of the present situation;

    c. that this information makes it possible to formulate expectations with respect to the future situation.

    d. that it is possible, in the light of knowledge concerning the expected future situation, to make those particular decisions that will *cause* the present situation to be transformed during an interval (x) into the forecasted (expected) future situation.

Among the questionable lessons this kind of planning teaches are: that human action, which is bunched up (here) in the area of "transforming decisions," will not affect the environment in any significant way that has not been "forecast;" that the future, therefore, will be virtually surprise-free, and will conform to a structure known beforehand; and that all human action can be organized so as to achieve gradual adaptation to minimal change. Implicit, is that the ends (values) are constant, fully or widely shared, and consciously known. Also implicit is that purpose is strongly channelled; that options are few; and that the impact of attained goals will be either negligible or uniform and thus permit *a priori* knowledge of outcomes.

This rather cursory critique of the historical, and still

practiced modes of planning is sufficient for us to conclude, at least for the moment, that so far people have generally planned on the assumption that the teleological elements of the action system were *given*. This assumption effectively excludes any viable consideration or reappraisal, especially of values and purpose, as well as any effort to make them consonant with either the current situation or a desired future situation which is conceived as differing from the present.

The main lesson we can draw from our brief historical survey is that all modes of past planning are basically geared to individual action, and represent implicit constraints upon it. The rationalization for such constraints being that no other way is available to a group or society to control *its* situation.

Among other things, this rationalization fails to take into account that the world is made up of many groups and societies that have different values and differing action dynamics. It is these differences that, through conflicts, varying rates of progress, etc., create what we called the "irrationality of the whole." Therefore, if that irrationality is to be reduced, or if individuals, groups, and other action generators are to be integrated we must reconsider most, if not all, our notions pertaining to planning. This brings us face to face with the perspectives that lie open before us in this field.

These perspectives are still somewhat hazy, for no definitive theory of planning has yet been created. Nevertheless, an increasing amount of thinking is beginning to crystallize around the problem, and it would appear that if efforts in search of solutions do not slacken it will be possible to evolve the necessary general hypotheses that can be put to the test of application and, thereby, of verification.

To understand the main thrusts of this new thinking, we must begin by addressing ourselves to the nature of what we call the "future." The term itself is so bandied about today in popular parlance that it is easy to forget that as a concept it is elusive, many-sided, and far from clear.

We noted that past modes of planning, including the orthodox, tended by and large to make the future as closely similar to the present as possible. This effort induces one (i) to make decisions in the light of current options; and (ii) to try to guess what the configuration of the major givens of the present are going to look like at a later time, and then make those decisions that will permit adaptation to such an assumed future situation. These two preoccupations indicate, with reference to our Figure 4, for example, that planning is always directed toward the present, and that the future, where the consequences of action crystallize, is, in fact, consistently ignored. These modes of planning by-pass, so to speak, the future, because the consequences of any single act can no longer be foreseen at a distance. The situation has become too complex, and such a multitude of acts intermesh with such a multitude of other acts that their combined result must be radically different from anything one can predict. Or to put it another way: beyond a certain time horizon our objectives and goals lose their differentiating characteristics and our objectives actually become absorbed by our goals. And once again we are prisoners of the present, of the short-range, of the current situation.

This state of affairs is no longer acceptable. Whether we can predict them or not, our actions do have consequences that are long-range; and by acting solely in the short-range we cannot imbue the total system with any kind of rationality. We remain an unintegrated "whole." And therefore, we ask ourselves, by what means can the future be viably reintroduced into the action system and thus into planning discourse? The prime answer is: by *willing* it. But how can a future be willed when so many different agents of action enter into play, and how can the individual action systems be coordinated so as to create, construct, invent, and bring about a willed future? This is the central challenge of modern planning discourse.

One way to confront this challenge is to revive the notion of "objectives." Returning again to Figure 4, we see that objectives operate as follows: (i) they are governed by "ends", that is, values; (ii) they are also governed by a long-term spectrum of options which the consequences of action create; (iii) adjusted, in this way, by the interplay of two sources of information—present values, and future consequences defined as preferred outcomes—they dictate goals. (The latter being always located in the field of present and known options.)

This manner of establishing objectives worked, as we have seen, for the Neolithic Hunter; he made an axe in order to be able, subsequently, to cut wood and protect himself against the cold season—such protection being one aspect of his need to survive. It worked because he had no doubts concerning his values—having but a single one, survival—that dictated his objective; he had no doubt that winter was coming, for experience had taught him about certain regularities in nature; he had no doubt that since wood was, we suppose, plentiful, he could cut it in sufficient quantities to survive if he had a good axe. In a barely populated world the consequences attendant upon his action, though of vital import to him, had a negligible effect on the general environment.

Now, let's place ourselves at the beginning of the twentieth century and consider the invention and production of automobiles. We find: (i) this was undertaken to satisfy several values — innovation and problem-solving; making transportation more flexible by affording greater mobility to individuals; application of various known technologies; (ii) the initial objectives might have been rather ill-defined aside from, perhaps increased mobility, and again, perhaps, making money; (iii) the eventual consequences that the objectives should have clarified, and been influenced by, were unknown and ignored.

However, once the innovation had demonstrated itself to be a success and cars in great numbers started to be produced, all hidden consequences began to stream forth. At first slowly, then with amazing speed the industrial structure of many countries changed drastically, and a whole new pattern of living and working—a pattern dependent on automobile production and usage—came into being. The steel and oil industries as well as component supplier industries grew to vast proportions. Roads and highways had to be built, which required that resources be used in one way rather than another. Methods of mass production were refined and the assembly-line was adopted, both creating a brand new set of labor problems. Employment patterns changed. And as cars became cheaper and more generally available, they, themselves, came to represent a value transcending that of mere transportation; they became a status symbol. However, these very major events were merely the first wave of consequences generated by the automobile. The second wave has been even more dramatic, for the automobile was superimposed on societies whose infrastructure (as we would call it today) was basically agricultural. The cities, which the automobile gradually overran, had usually been built to serve the need of that agricultural mode of life. They were not meant for cars—nor, as we find now, was our planet's atmosphere indifferent to the pollutants emitted by the internal combustion engine. The story is too well known to require further details. What must, however, be done is to ask the question which this example raises vis-à-vis planning.

It can be cogently argued that the objectives for making the automobile, though never adequately articulated, represented some sort of good. We may grant that they were nurtured by the particular values and outlooks of a particular age. But it is also clear that these objectives were not conceived in the light of the innovation's possible consequences.

Here several questions confront us: Could the full spectrum of consequences be foreseen? If so, did they still correspond in terms of overall costs and benefits to any notion of the good? Had the findings been negative regarding the good, would we have stopped ourselves from making automobiles?

I believe that the answer to the first question is a qualified "no." Qualified, in that not all, but at least some of the consequences could have been envisioned; whereas the others could have been worked out as the evolutionary dynamics of the situation created by the automobile gained momentum. (What I am saying here does not apply equally to the Neolithic Hunter; *he* could not have foreseen that the sharp-edge he had learned to transform into an axe would one far-off day denude part of the planet of trees, and cause all sorts of problems! He lacked access to the information that the twentieth century innovators and producers could have procured had they been concerned with looking for it.)

The answers to the other questions are also "no," and less qualifiedly so. Our short range rationality had never created the requisite outlook and institutions that would even permit the raising of such questions, let alone the answering of them. And furthermore, that same short-range rationality had taught us that if something was technically feasible and appeared economically sound it *was a virtue to bring it* to fruition.

All this is not to criticize the automobile per se, but to help us understand the workings of planning, and through such understanding, define its dynamic.

I believe the example shows that the main shortcomings of contemporary planning are to be found in the activity of several elements of the human action system, namely: (i) that values are assumed always to be stable, whereas, in a situation of rapid change, they are not; (ii) that this belief distorts our perception of reality and makes our minds and methods of thought responsive to "promlems" rather than generative of "anticipated solutions;" (iii) that our knowledge—this follows from the first point—is almost entirely means-directed and, therefore, imposes those options that known means have already created, on our decisions; (iv) that such over-emphasis on means distorts our purpose, doing so by convincing us that only those options immediately present, virtually visible to the naked eye, can be chosen and, therefore, "willed;" (v) that, finally, all of the foregoing dictates objectives that are not only formulated by past values, but are wholly innocent of any consideration of consequences—overall consequences—ensuing from our decisions and actions.

If the foregoing is correct, then we can proceed by defining the changes that we must bring to our notions of planning in order to make them consonant with the current and emerging situation. Thus:

a. Planning must so change that the decision process it represents accepts reconsideration of the value-premises underlying every decision.

b. Planning must so change that the decision process it represents includes mechanisms of choice; of choosing, not only from among the immediate outcomes derivable from available, known, options—but, also, from among alternative, imagined and willed long-range consequences of decisions and action.

c. Planning must so change that the decision process it represents will subordinate the problem of appropriate means, and of relevant short-range action patterns to (a) and (b) above.

The action and decision process involved in these three points is outlined in Figure 9. This diagram brings out the following points: (i) situation and purpose, in conjunction with each other, constitute the action-generating elements within the reality/environment context; (ii) the first activity in the process is the consideration of ends, hence of long-term consequences in the light of value-judgments; (iii) the first decision concerning objectives is made in the light of such consequence and value assessments—if the best determinable alternative consequence does not satisfy the long-term value requirements, the system *closes* at the objective-setting phase, feeds back into purpose so that a reconsideration of the proposed action becomes possible and so that a new action pattern embodying a different, more acceptable, consequence can be visualized and undertaken; (iv) if the objective(s) do satisfy the value/consequence requirements, then the process continues to its subsequent phases through the setting of goals and decisions concerning the most relevant means, which, then, are directed to the selected outcome that must, as a matter of course, be consonant with the long-term consequence that was initially defined; (v) it is, finally, in the light of consequences thus chosen that the outcome, governed by the goal and the means, feeds back into the situation and changes reality in a manner that was *planned*.

What, among other things, such a process does is to satisfy two of the most fundamental requirements of modern planning; namely, that the internal decision system should be so organized that each decision rationalizes and facilitates the next decision; and that information about the present should be derived from the consequences of action rather than from immediate results or outcomes. This last point also permits a new understanding of optimal resource use within an enlarged and lengthened action/time horizon.

Such is, in its theoretical outline, the needed (and, hopefully, emerging) planning system. I say *system*, because that is what it clearly is. It is, in fact, a complex, dynamic, hierarchical system of human action. In the next few pages, we shall try to understand what this means.

IV. PLANNING AS A HIERARCHICAL SYSTEM

A. The Notion of Hierarchy

"Hierarchy" means many things, and many of its fundamental aspects are dealt with in Paul Weiss' paper which
opens this book.* Therefore, I shall try mainly to look at
this rather complex idea from the viewpoint of the planning
concept that we have begun to outline.

The notion of hierarchy, in systems theory, describes a
particular view of a system's structure. It, therefore, qual-
ifies a given system's organization. But this is not all, for
hierarchy also exists at a deeper as well as a more dynamic level: it governs the system's structure and operation
through the interaction of the special relationships that it
creates. In so doing it becomes the mechanism that defines
not only structural configurations, but also the manner in
which such structures do, in fact, behave.

When we speak of structures that "behave," we are talk-
ing of systems whose elements are related to each other in
more than one dimension—systems that comprise several
levels wherein the function of each level is in some definite
sense integrated with all the others, but different from all
the others. In such systems we also find that a part of the
hierarchical structure is an organization of communications
between levels, which forces us to face the important problem of communication across system boundaries and levels.
Furthermore, we find that some levels of the system are
determined by others, whereas the contrary is not true.
Still further, we discover that each level could be considered
as a system unto itself, and that the *whole*—the all encompassing system represents a highly complex independent
entity whose behavior cannot be causally derived from the
summed up behavior of its levels.

All these observations give us an idea of the nature and

* See above, pp.

complexity of hierarchical systems, in general. To make the
description more comprehensible, I shall use an example
that was developed by M. Polanyi, and that has become
something of a classic.[1]

In this example Polanyi views language, or rather the
composition and articulation of a literary text, as a hierarchically organized system. First, we have the generation
of letters—an alphabet, which is an initial system possessing its own laws, concepts, and operations. Second, we have
the rule-governed grouping of letters that form words;
this, too, is a separate system that has its own structure
(vocabulary), etc. Third, words become organized into sentences—another system, and one capable of expressing statements in accordance with a particular grammar, syntax and
semantics. Fourth, we have a text whose value, or literary
worth, is judged by aesthetic values that prevail in the
language, culture, fashion, etc., current in the specific environment wherein all the foregoing has occurred, and this
is yet another system that operates in relation to its own
elements and in its particular terms.

The important things to note in this excellent example
are: (i) that we have one system formed by four systems
that could be seen as independent; (ii) that the system is
hierarchical inasmuch as the creation of letters does not
and cannot govern the rules of the system above it, which
is a vocabulary; nor is a vocabulary, by itself, capable of
defining the structure of a grammar, a syntax or semantics,
and finally, neither of these can directly suggest the values
whereby the final outcome will be judged as a work of art.
However, if we go the other way around we find that, given
a system of aesthetics, we can find out how the syntax and
semantics ought to be used to satisfy it; that given a grammar, a syntax and semantics we will know how to use a
vocabulary, and that given a vocabulary, we can develop an

[1] "Life's Irreducible Structure," *Science*, 1968, 160: 1308-1312.

alphabet. Thus, although the component systems can, in some sense, be considered as independent from each other, they are, nevertheless, hierarchically organized when viewed in relation to the end: a text that can be valued as a literary composition. Hence, the end-system is the *organizing system* of the *whole,* while the others either organize themselves and/ or the system that is immediately below them (and are, of course, organizationally influenced by the system(s) above them—from which they proceed); (iii) this does not mean that each independent system does not have its own internal hierarchy, its own rules, objectives, goals, etc.; (iv) nor does it mean that the system of values—that which organizes the whole—could have any meaning apart from the others, any more than any one of component systems could have meaning apart from the systems that are subordinate to them.

Forgetting the specific reference (literary composition) of this example, let us now try to visualize the hierarchical structure of such a complex system in the abstract. When we do this we shall, I believe, come up with something resembling Figure 10. This figure, which appears rather complicated, is simply explained.

There are (n) systems considered, three of which are named (1) (2) and (3). The numbered systems together are said to constitute a "whole"—that is, a hierarchically organized structure. In relation to the others, System 1 is postulated to be the *organizing system.* In relation to System 1, all the others can be described as *instrumental systems.* The definitions of each type are as follows:

(17) In a hierarchical structure an *organizing system* is the system whose ends or values govern and determine the behavior of the whole structure.

(18) In a hierarchical structure *instrumental systems* are those systems whose ends or values are determined in such a manner as to fulfill, beside their own ends, the ends or values of the organizing system.

The above is further clarified if we remember that:

- In hierarchical structures the objectives and goals of the organizing system represent the objectives and goals of the *whole* structure; whereas the objectives and goals of instrumental systems are set and attained with the aim of providing information to the knowledge/means elements of the next higher level, and ultimately, to that of the organizing system.

- For a hierarchical structure to exist, it is not generally necessary that any of its component systems be symmetrical as to their elements or contexts, nor can the principles of operation applicable to any component system be necessarily derived from principles that are applicable to the other component systems.*

- For any component system of a hierarchical structure to attain its goal, it is necessary that the component systems below it function correctly.

- It is not possible to understand a hierarchically structured whole system with reference to any of its component systems if the latter are taken separately. It is, however, possible to say that "starting from any given [system] stratum, understanding of a system increases by crossing (boundaries) : moving down the hierarchy one obtains a more detailed explanation, while moving up the hierarchy one obtains a deeper understanding of its significance [or meaning]."[1]

To conclude this explanatory section, we should perhaps add a word about terminology. In the literature on hierachical systems, one encounters expressions like "subsystem," "level," "layer," "stratum," etc., by which different authors explicate various aspects of such structures. The concention

* This statement is correct despite the fact that in order not to over-complicate it, I have shown symmetrically constructed system levels in Figure 10.

[1] M. D. Mesarovic and D. Macko, "Scientific Theory of Hierarchical Systems" in *Hierarchical Structures*, L. L. Whyte, A. G. Wilson, D. Wilson, Eds., American Elsevier Publishing Co., New York, 1969.

I have chosen is to use the term "whole system" with reference to large-scale, complex hierarchical structures, and to distinguish various types of systems within them. I refer to the relative position of each such system within the structure by using the word "level." My reason for choosing the first convention is that, with respect to a theory of planning, we shall apply the notion of hierarchical structures to fields of events that are sufficiently large as to constitute entire systems in their own right. I adopted the second convention because the term "level" is quite general and gives us a great deal of freedom without forcing us to enter into technical details that would be either irrelevant, or confusing, to our particular argument.

B. Hierarchical Structure of Planning

In the latter part of Section III, I noted three structural and substantive changes that I feel need to be considered to bring our present-day practices of planning into consonance with present-day realities. These changes flow directly from the action patterns we have been exploring throughout this paper, and it is relative to the planning system they suggest that I shall now try to explore the hierarchical relationships which exist in such a system. But first, we shall have to outline the entire structure of the kind of plan which comes into view as a result of the changes that have been advocated.

Normative Planning

To begin with, we said that planning must be so conceived that the decision process it represents accepts reconsideration of the value premises underlying every decision. This, in itself, adds a new level to the planning structure we have called "orthodox." We shall name this new level *normative planning*. The main activity at this level is the definition of ends, in the light of a value analysis of the consequences that one can determine as the probable long-term outcomes of any action one is considering. Basically, normative planning should reveal what, under given circumstances and in view of known and imaginable factors, *ought* to be done.

In essence, then, normative planning is done with reference to ends and their value-content, and is aimed at the clarification of the consequences of proposed action(s) within a hypothetical time interval and some whole environment or situation. When such consequences have been made clear, the normative plan determines whether they will ultimately be "good" or "bad" for some whole environment, and not merely for individual sectoral generators of the plan—be the latter a person, an organization, a city, a region, or a nation-state, etc. The traditional argument against normative planning has been that since values are given, they automatically enter into any form of planning. The fact that they exist is perfectly true. The trouble is that they exist implicitly; they are never consciously reviewed; and we can no longer be sure that our inherited values (or their current interpretations) will, in fact, yield consequences that are good for some definable "whole" situation. Hence, it is absolutely necessary to question them and to reconsider them *explicitly* as part of the planning process. As matters now stand, we simply do not know—nor can we know in so complicated a situation as ours—whether the values on which, for example, our present institutions are based will produce desirable consequences—desirable being defined in a new and unfamiliar context. And since individual entities are part of the whole interresponsive system of reality, we cannot even determine on the basis of our current implicit values, if what we think is good or desirable for individual selves or entities, actually is so. We cannot, because valuing the whole is not an explicit (often not even an implicit) value for us. What this means is of great importance. It means that: planning must be viewed as a decision-making activity under true uncertainty; namely, that we have to face up to and accept that information about consequences lies at the end of the process (the same as in creative action), and that it cannot be *predicted*. However, sets of alternative consequences can be visualized and assessed as to their desirability. Then choices are made from among them and the action system is directed toward those ends as such choices dictate. Hence the normative plan should be seen, not as an instrument of prediction but of control. Control in this sense is achieved by continuously adjusting our ends, our values, to change, and by coordinating the rest of the plan in the light of such adjustments. This suggests that at the highest level of planning, the result is not really a plan, but continuous planning activity. Planning then becomes an integral motivator and generator of action at whatever level that action is envisioned.

To be effective, normative planning needs to be informed by values from which its norms of control are derived. It is admittedly very difficult in a world so fragmented and polarized as ours, to invent new values out of whole cloth and to impose them upon people whose traditions, cultures and ways of life are so various, and whose objectives and goals often are, or appear, so divergent. Our traditional values, whose more general historical expressions are: love (in the social sphere), truth (in the sphere of scientific knowledge), and utility (in the techno-economic sphere), have been operationally interpreted in so many strange and seemingly contradictory ways throughout the ages, that they no longer affect consequences of human action in a manner consonant with their original meanings. However, a new situation has now come upon us. Because of our inability, or maybe our unwillingness, to worry about consequences of action, we find ourselves on the verge of reviving the oldest and most general value of all: survival. If this be so, as I believe it is, we will have come full circle. But, although we may well have come full circle, our situation is new and imposes new terms of reference upon our actions, for it is the rapid deterioration of our natural and social environment that is now raising the issue of our survival as a species. Under these conditions it might not be too presumptuous to propose a new general value that should be acceptable to virtually all people, and would not add another divisive factor to those that are already pulling us asunder. Such a value would be: survival through the achievement of a global, dynamic ecological balance. (Ecology being understood, here, as encompassing all the major interactions that human beings experience — interactions with the natural environment, social, political and economic interaction, as well as psycho-social, individual, etc. relationships.)*

It seems to me that action and planning in the light of such a general value might gradually lead to greater consonance between individual objectives and goals by providing them with a global base; and that further, it would help us begin to evolve the next generation of institutions— institutions within which all the needed operational modalities and norms derivable from such a value could be worked out over time, without ideological ruptures and the violence-breeding divisiveness that would exacerbate, or at best keep us prisoners in, the state of confusion and disorder where we now find ourselves.

Whether this particular "value-base" is generally accepted or not, does not change the fact that in a planning system which aims at theoretical completeness, and is addressed to "whole situations," normative planning must be considered as the *organizing system* of any plan's hierarchical structure. And let us remember that at this normative level, decisions are directed toward what "ought" to be done. At this level, planning is guided by decisions that define the "oughts" to which the entire system's "ends," "purposes,"

---

* For a more detailed discussion of these points, see Hasan Ozbekhan, *Op. Cit.*

"objectives," and "goals"—the *technological elements*—are subordinated.

Strategic Planning

The second change we proposed in Section III was the inclusion into the planning system of choice-mechanisms that would permit the visualization that exists between known options and their possible alternative consequences. What this means is that, aside from ends and their value consequences, in the long run we must establish procedures for goal-setting in which goal(s)—that is, time-specific outcomes—are related to their more distant consequences.

These procedures are embedded in a different level than the normative plan. They are part of what we shall call *strategic planning*. Strategic plans define those decisions which determine what *can* be done—given a time interval and a whole situation.

Thus, while normative planning is directed toward the analysis and selection of objectives, the main function of the strategic plan is the setting of goals for the whole system. Again, while the normative plan is consequence-oriented, relative to the value-content of consequences, the strategic plan is outcome-oriented — keeping in mind, of course, that any outcome will have to be consonant with and subordinated to the normative constraints established at the higher level.

Goal-setting (the definition of what "can" be done as derived from what "ought" to be done) involves: (i) goal selection with reference to options which are known and available, but that must be reconfigured to make them fit desirable consequences; (ii) selection and design of the means for attaining such goal(s)—this involves the definition of appropriate operating policies, including the structuring of the operational controls that will govern implementation; the determination of resources that are needed; the allocation of the resources among the organizational components that will carry out the plan as a whole; and the design of the implementing organization itself.

Thus, to repeat, strategic decisions are those that define (or re-define) what ought to be done in terms of what *can* be done, given the immediate constraints which pertain to the goal (open options), and the means that are available. A whole plan's strategic system, therefore, represents the main *instrumental system* within which action patterns are selected, and feasibility determined.

Operational Planning

The last change we proposed was that, in planning, implementation—i.e., the application of the means—should be subordinated to the requirements that arise from normatively established objectives and to whole system goals set at the strategic decision level. This implies that the strategic planning system has as its underpinning another lower *instrumental system* that we can call *operational planning.* The prime function of this system is the implementation of decisions that have been reached at higher levels. However, such implementation is never automatic; confronted with an ever fluid situation, day-to-day modifications in applying available means and resources must be made. All decisions of "how" to attain the goal are made at this operational level of the overall planning system. It is at this level that what *will* be done to satisfy the "oughts" and the "can," that have been established at higher levels, is determined in an ongoing manner.

I do not believe that it would be fruitful to dwell at greater length on the operational planning system—especially, since the technical literature on the subject is rather large and well known. I shall, therefore, proceed directly to the discussion of the "whole" planning system.

The "Whole" Planning System

In the hope of constructing an integrated image of the foregoing three-level planning system, and thereby making

it easier to understand, I have translated the abstract outline of a generic hierarchical system (Fig. 10) into the
structure of planned action, as just described, in Figure 11.

The two diagrams are the same except that in Figure 11,
I have re-introduced all the visual symbols that were employed from the beginning to describe the experiential source
of an action system, and added the image of anticipated
alternative consequences of action as a subjective element,
existing in the head of one or several actors at a given
present moment in time. Such an image, the composite of
available options and possible consequences, always exists
in the present and in the mind. It forms part of a specific
situation, comprising defined knowledge, given values, and
a particular perception of reality; for it is in the present
and in the mind that purpose and will and anticipations
operate. The aim of planning is to control those future
events that will ensue from any contemplated action, in
such a manner that their consequences upon the moving
present will be as consonant with what one wants the present to be, as possible.

Within the overall or "whole" plan, each of the three
hierarchically related levels, that we have just described,
represents a particular set of meanings and controls which
lead to particular classes of action. It is evident that we
must make a number of explicatory assumptions about how
these various factors interconnect to form a functionally
integrated and directed entity. To do this, we shall have to
remember first that a plan is a system of human action and
that, as any system does, it operates within a set of embedding conditions, the sum of which are defined as its
environment. The latter, as we have repeatedly seen, has
many constituent elements and laws (both natural and man
made) that shape events, in an always changing conjuncture which is the situation. Therefore, in order to stipulate the above mentioned assumptions we must ask ourselves: what are the meanings, controls and activities gen-

erated by this environment/situation that impinge upon the plan; how do they become translated into the plan, or reflected by it?

To answer this complex question in a way that remains within the scope of our subject, it is easiest to look at the problem from within the structure of the planning system, and to look at it from the viewpoint of feedback in conjunction with hierarchy—that is, from the viewpoint of control mechanisms in conjunction with system organizing mechanisms.

These two concepts suggest that each distinct level of action is controlled by feedback emanating from a different level of the hierarchy. And, on more intensive consideration, it would seem that this controlling feedback, itself, forms a hierarchy whose operations are of great interest. The way in which each level of the feedback process exercises its particular mode of control is dependent upon the functional need of the lower levels; and, on the other hand, the functional needs of each level are controlled by the next higher level.

Hence, the control structure of the plan is twofold: (i) control imposed by laws that are specific to the internal, or constituent elements of the plan; (ii) control that emanates from the laws that govern the environment/situation within which the plan exists and operates. This dual flow of control must not only be understood as the assertion of power over a subordinate activity by a higher one, but rather as an *infusion of meaning* into the lower levels.

With these points in mind, we can now both summarize and enlarge our conception of planning, as follows:

1. A plan is a complex, dynamic system—an event-controlling structure whose function is to effect, in its environment (which is another complex dynamic system), the kind of organized change that general values define as desirable.

2. The structure of the plan has three hierarchically related levels:

   (a) an operational level at which the plan is mainly mechanistic in character

   (b) a higher, strategic level at which the plan is anticipatory in character

   (c) a still higher, normative level at which the plan is telic in character.

3. All plans fulfill their functions under two general types of control:

   (a) controls that pertain specifically to each level of their structure

   (b) controls that emanate from the laws—both natural and human—that control the environment.

4. These controls work in the following way:

   (a) the normative plan, to fulfill its specific function, depends on the operations of all the levels below it. It delimits the operations of the strategic plan by imposing on it a boundary (the notion and function of "strategy") that makes it serve the norms which have been established through it;

   (b) the strategic plan, to fulfill its specific function, relies on the mechanics of the operational plan and on the environmental inputs below it. It reduces the scope of the operational plan by imposing a boundary (the notion and function of "operations") on it, that brings it into the service of the strategies defined as parts of it;

   (c) the operational plan, to fulfill its specific function, relies on inputs from the environment. It limits the scope of, while ascribing specific meaning to, these inputs by imposing boundaries upon them (e.g. selectivity in the light of criteria such as resources, or limitations inherent in operating procedures and methods) that cause them to be brought into the service of the operations defined by the plan.

5. In this way, control can be seen as transmitted downward to the most concrete level of environmental elements.

This control, when imposed upon objects and events, is what produces change in such objects and events—planned change. It follows that control and power of this kind must entail a *meaning* (the meaning which "purpose" embodies) that is transmitted by it from the normative level of the plan, through the strategic, and down to the operational. (Hence, a plan that is solely operational, or purely strategic, is actually devoid of meaning, although it often appears to have meaning because it always exists in an implicit normative context that, by association, shades it with meaning).

6. The fundamental problem in planning is to endow the plan's inner levels with explicit meaning, and to bridge the boundaries between plan and environment with that explicit meaning.

7. Nor can the above problem be solved by arbitrarily ascribing meanings to operational plans and trying to translate these meanings upward into strategies, and then into norms. The hierarchical organization of plans prevents this, because:

    (a) the content and operations of normative plans *cannot* be deduced from the principles governing strategic plans;

    (b) the content and operations of strategic plans *cannot* be deduced from the principles governing operational plans;

    (c) the content and operations of operational plans *cannot* be deduced from the partial or sectoral requirements of the environment.

8. Hence, we must conclude that, both in terms of control and in terms of meaning, it is the highest level in the plan's structure which dictates or determines the information content of the lower levels, whereas the contrary is not true.

The foregoing describes the hierarchical structure of

planning from the viewpoint of greatest generality—control and meaning—and provides an idea of how the organizing system of the plan (i.e., the normative level) dictates and determines the information content of the instrumental systems (i.e., the strategic and operational levels).

Now hierarchical dimensions will be found in the planning system's internal decision structure as well as in its functional structure.

With reference to the planning system's decision structure, we find that it corresponds to the classical, functional hierarchy of decision problems under conditions describable as those of "true uncertainty." (Fig. 12)*

The major decision points in the planning structure we have developed are suggested by the structure's hierarchical organization. They are: (i) decisions regarding ends (values and norm-seeking) that provide information about the hypotheses one can make concerning consequences of action and, therefore, concerning the problem-solving strategies that are appropriate; (ii) decisions regarding whole system goals that have been chosen in consonance with the accepted norms, and decisions regarding available or applicable means, which, together, will optimize both action and the learning process that such action feeds back into the decision continuum—at this level uncertainty should be reduced; (iii) decisions regarding the ongoing control of the chosen action process under conditions that have been specified by the above structural levels—this, further, involves the search for new courses of action as the situation changes, i.e., while consequences become crystallized, and learning at higher levels increases.

Thus, the function of the control (and search) level is to define action m in the light of outside information, and of information received from higher levels as well. In plan-

---

* This figure is adapted directly from Mesarovic and Macko, *Op. Cit.*, where the reader will also find a brief, highly interesting set-theoretic treatment of this problem.

ning, these tasks correspond to "administrative" functions. At the next higher level—that of optimizing action and learning—the task is to specify the uncertainty of the entire system by defining the goal of the system, and thus make it possible for the lower administrative functions to operate. In an environment of change, such as the one we have assumed throughout, this requires an optimized correspondence of goals and means, and the alteration of either set as learning occurs, and as the situation and the norms, established at a higher level, dictate. Planning subsumes these functions under the notion of "goal-setting." At the self-organizing level, the ends that the whole decision-making process aims to reach are defined with reference to values. The intrinsic goal of this particular system-level is to establish those norms that define the consonance between ends (the value relations) and the consequences of contemplated action, and also to seek and select norms that can govern the entire decision/action process. In functional terms, activities of this kind are named "policy making."

In connection with the above, it is important to take note of a point that is seldom, if ever, mentioned in planning literature; it concerns "lead-time" in decision-making, "learning" at the strategic search level, and "goal attainment." The point can best be made by viewing planning as a cybernetic system in which goal is defined as the system's "output," objective and means are defined as "controlled inputs," and events comprising a situation are defined as "uncontrolled inputs." Neither objective nor means are static. They incessantly interact with the unfolding action, and they both influence, and are influenced by, the events that impinge on the action process as it gets underway. This interval of time between intention and performance is what we called "lead-time." During it, many circumstances may, and do, arise, which without necessarily altering either the objective or the nature or quantity of the means, nevertheless create changes in the *level* of "goal

attainment." The process of "learning" in the strategic
search system also affects the level of "goal attainment,"
for during this process, strategic and operational decisions
are modified as planning and doing become intermeshed
in action. All these new occurrences will alter the actors'
perception at many levels, or points, of the system, and
their conception of the basic goal may change—again, not
necessarily in nature, but in attainment-level and in time.
Therefore, as the action proceeds, one of the most vital functions of the strategic and operational systems is to determine
what changes in goal-attainment are tolerable. How much
change can occur without too great a deviation from the
whole-system goal that was originally set? To determine
this, one must conceive as part of the planning and decision-
making process, a pattern of ordering that is not inflexible.
The ordering originates from an initial whole-system goal,
but then may be deflected from it either by better optimiza-
tions, or by distortive sub-optimizations. (This latter, too,
is a form of hierarchical ordering that inheres to the process
of goal-attainment).

Figure 13 tries to depict such a range of possible outcome
levels in terms of a goal. It indicates that given an initial
plan, so conceived as to attain the whole system goal in a
specified time interval (Phase IV), with certain definite
objectives and certain definite means, one can imagine a
number of modifications that might intervene and affect the
ordering of the initial plan. For instance: during the preparatory lead-time one might think that the same goal could
have been attained in Phase II and at a higher level (Level
+1), and conclude that this solution was rejected because
Phase II is too early and cannot satisfy the situation's other
requirements; or one might think that the goal could be
reached at Phase III on Level +2, with a somewhat longer
lead-time—in this case a cost/benefit analysis of such a lead-
time would be necessary to ascertain whether this strategy
(Phase III/Level +2) might be better than the one orig-

inally adopted. On the other hand, one would not accept the plan that attains the goal at almost beyond Phase IV/ Level −1, for its lead-time is identical to that of the initial plan and is, therefore, a sub-optimization. However, the plan with a very long lead-time, that which attains the goal at Phase III/Level −2 might be acceptable if the goal at Level −2 is considered acceptable. It would appear, on the face of it, that the plan which attains the goal at Phase III/Level −2 is considered acceptable. Here, at first glance, it would appear that the plan which attains the goal at Phase III/Level +2 would be the best one of all if the longer lead-time it require can be tolerated. No final answer can, of course, be given since the feedback loops and interim learning patterns are not shown in the illustration. Despite this, we have here clear indication that another hierarchy exists in all plans, i.e., that which orders and correlates lead-time both with learning, in the strategic search system, and with levels of goal attainment.

To conclude we must look at the hierarchy of functions that exist in the planning system I have outlined.

Within such a system, three general classes of functions must be recognized and considered: (1) *administrative functions* that insure the system's internal coherence and govern, at the "operational" level, the implementation of the decisions taken at the two higher levels; (2) *goal-setting functions* which I shall view as corresponding to executive decision-making at the "strategic" level of our model; (3) *norm-seeking functions* which are the core of "normative" planning, and correspond to what usually goes under the name of policy making.

It is important to note the differences that exist between this particular scheme and what I have called "orthodox" planning. In the latter, two major types of functional relations are found. One is the administrative/operational, which is almost the same as what I am proposing. The second is a somewhat confused relation that is said to prevail between the allocational/strategic functions. We have seen earlier, that I do not feel this particular relation to be either operationally meaningful or particularly helpful to our understanding of planning. While executive decision-making does play a strong role in allocating resources, this process can hardly be divorced from that of goal-setting. Hence, I consider goal-setting as the heart of strategic planning. Orthodox practice, however, sees goal-setting as part not of planning, but of policy making. In my scheme, not only is goal-setting part of planning, it is intrinsic to the executive level of functions, and not to the policy level.

Moreover, I maintain that planning does include the policy-making phase that I have called normative planning. Here the core of the argument is that policies are not just part of a meaningful planning process; policy making does *not* consist of goal-setting—it consists of norm-seeking. As one can see from this brief outline, the differences between the proposed scheme and orthodox planning are quite fundamental except, perhaps, insofar as the administrative/operational functional relations are concerned.

V. CONCLUSIONS

A. Large Systems and their Regulation

The planned action model we have just outlined represents a time dimensional decision process that is designed to integrate and organize rational behavior with those fast changing and intricately intermeshed events whose totality we have called "situation." We have found such integration and organization of action to be increasingly necessary if we are to control the disorder that inheres to the situation. At present, we can no longer exert any meaningful control over the disorder that now has become endemic to our environment, because our traditional mechanisms for coordinating action are so fragmented that, if anything, they augment disorder rather than diminish it.

What is left for us to do in these concluding pages is to review, somewhat more deeply than we have been able to do previously, the fundamental problems that the kind of control we have proposed entails. We hope that such a review will make it possible not only to clarify further certain aspects of the arguments we have advanced, but also to determine what changes in our outlook and intellectual habits still remain to be made.

By analyzing the situation we can try to define its salient characteristics; then we can seek to determine what conditions are required to make our notion of planned action operational.

First of all, from almost any perspective we may choose to look at it, the situation appears to correspond to what can be called a *large system*.

Of course, the qualifier "large," being relative, is imprecise; yet it is not inaccurate, for our situation today displays an unmistakable tendency towards becoming *global*, or, as Teilhard de Chardin called it, "planetized." This leads us to a very important point, namely, that the situation (those embedding conditions which both generate human action and are in great part generated by it) is composed of events whose boundaries can no longer be defined in terms of our traditional labels or categories. For instance, we can no longer say that we *know* what such long familiar notions as education, health, poverty, abundance, over- (or under-) population, capitalism, socialism, democracy, the university, the international balance of payments, war, peace, industrialism, the economy, etc., really mean. When I say we don't know what they mean, I am trying to convey the fact that we are no longer clear—or as clear as we formerly seemed to be—about their causal and functional dynamics, their interactions, or the synergies that nurture and animate them. All these situational components intermix and intermesh in such an extraordinarily complex conjuncture, that we ignore where or when any of them begin or end. And our ignorance goes far deeper than our inability to recognize the boundaries of such events. We have now reached a point where we can no longer define, that is, understand the internal structure of these events if we look at their structures singularly and individually. Hence we cannot hope to solve the problems (control the disorder) that such events create by labeling them or by attacking them linearly.

To give an example: the world-wide famine that is generally expected to occur during the last two or three decades of this century is not something that is amenable to solution through the mere production of more food. This much our calculations have shown us. Nor can it be forestalled by the adoption of better agricultural methods. This suggests that the *concept* "agriculture," as understood throughout the ages and still in our own day, is no longer sufficient; that the solutions which this heading comprises are inadequate, or even that they may address themselves to the wrong problem. What, then is the problem? In the light of present-day knowledge which, itself, is still tentative, speculative and fragmentary, it appears that the problem is *everything* —that what we classify under the title of world-famine is not a problem we can understand solely with reference to the state of being hungry insofar as large portions of the human race are concerned, but that it involves health, energy, education, institutions, population, technology, science, a reconsideration of world-wide production and distribution systems, the price mechanism, and so on.

The very same considerations apply as well if, instead of the problem called famine, we were to select any other labelled problem: health, education, politics, the various existing economic systems, ecology, etc. It is in the new patterns of interactivity among events, in their acceleration, in their unexpected configurations, and in their totally obscure interconnections that we encounter the phenomenon of globalization. Problems, to use a very meaningful but untranslatable French expression, have become agglutinated into one vast *problématique*. To me, all this suggests that the situation is developing into a world-wide system of events. If this view is correct, then it is clear that the situation as a whole must obviously be seen as a very *large* system, regardless of how we choose to measure such a system's size.

Even if we take a more traditional stance and consider reality in a somewhat more fragmented fashion—say, with reference to whole sets of phenomena that we describe under headings such as biology, psychology, economics, sociology, ecology, etc.—we are again confronted by systems of events, occurrences, and phenomena that are extremely large, in and of themselves.

The foregoing has been noted merely to support the contention that we are confronted with a situation whose dimensions are of a new order of magnitude, and whose complexity is equally great. If such, then, is the reality with which we must deal, our basic dilemma is that although we don't, as yet, have a body of knowledge that comprehends systems of this size and complexity, planned action is precisely meant to address itself to this type of massive conjuncture. Even when planning is, on the surface, directed to issues that appear much more limited in scope—say, corporate planning—it must be so conceived as to be capable of organizing action and vision in ways that are relevant to the whole system (situation) or, at any rate, to some whole component system (e.g., the economy, inclusive of its socio-political aspects).

From the standpoint of systems theory, that is from the standpoint of the methodology of planning, such a *problématique* raises two major issues that are common to all large systems. One is the question of "size"; the second is a conglomerate question that has to do with the concept "whole"—with the fact that we must deal not only with large systems, but also, and especially, with total ones.

Concerning the matter of *size*, we must point out that

powerful arguments have been advanced, mainly by people engaged in so-called "practical" pursuits and day-by-day problem solving, to the effect that the problems involved in very large systems cannot really be visualized in any meaningful way, let alone resolved. This manner of reasoning tends to encourage the use of overly analytic methods and the breakup of problems into ever smaller component units so that relations between such units eventually become perceivable. These relations can then be manipulated in accordance with the rules of classical logical theory, and lead to solutions.

The argument has a certain attraction in that it reflects our old tested ways of reasoning and solving problems. We feel comfortable with it, especially when we think of the many different levels of reality and complexity that large systems confront us with. Dealing with large systems fills us with awe, perhaps even some fear, but the comfort we draw from familiar analytic methods must not blind us to two basic facts: (i) these methods do not actually work—they help us neither to adapt sufficiently fast to our situation, nor to anticipate the consequences of our actions; and (ii) the argument itself is based on a wrong, or at least mistaken view of the situational problem, since its underlying premise is that the difficulty in understanding or tackling large systems inheres to the *size* of the system.

We have already dealt with the first point, but shall return to it when discussing the matter of wholes. The second point, however, must be dealt upon briefly. By implication this point indicates, that the size of systems is *not* the central difficulty we face with large systems; what we call "the systems approach" or "systems thinking" deals with *states* —the states of a system—and is, therefore, insensitive to the question of size. Here, it is important to keep in mind W. Ross Ashby's profound observation:

> "It is a peculiar advantage of the method of arguing about states, rather than the more usual variables,

that it requires no explicit mention of the system's number of parts; and theorems once proved true are true for systems of all sizes (provided of course that the systems conform to the suppositions made in the argument) ... *What is the main source of the difficulty is the variety of the disturbances that must be regulated against.*"[1]

Thus the real obstacle one encounters in planning is not the size of the systems one has to deal with—except perhaps at the mechanistic/administrative (i.e. operational level)— but in the quantity of required regulation. However, such quantity is limited by many factors, and especially by the choices that must be made both among alternative problem-areas and among alternative outcomes that are deemed desirable.

Obviously we shall have to come back to this question of "quantity of regulation" when we revert to a discussion of planning. Meanwhile, let us proceed to review the second issue we have noted as being important, namely, that of "whole systems" or that of "wholes."

Here, we find ourselves confronted with a very deep problem indeed. To repeat what we said a few pages earlier, the problem of wholes arises from the need to understand the situational system as a system, that is, in its entirety, if we are to understand the integrative and coordinating function of planning in the modern world.

The prime difficulty we encounter when we approach the problem of wholes is that we have no logic for dealing with it. The logic we do have i.e., the logic of relationships, is entirely inadequate for solving system problems—hence, the planning problems which are confronting us. Insofar as I know, work on this subject has been attempted mainly in the field of gestalt psychology and, more recently, in general logical theory especially by the logicians of the

---

[1] *An Introduction to Cybernetics*, Chapman and Hall, London, 1970. Italics in text.

Warsaw School.* Nevertheless, such efforts notwithstanding, no operationally applicable results have yet emerged, although principles that clarify the nature of the problem and indicate what needs to be done, have. The following outline of the problem is entirely based on the pioneering work of A. Angyal. This work, aside from its conciseness, has the great virtue of being extremely lucid and easy to understand.[1]

Angyal's main points are that: (1) A logic of wholes differs from our traditional methods of thought in that it does not deal with "relationships," as the term is usually interpreted, but with "some more adequate logical unit, representing an entirely different logical genus . . . suitable to the treatment of wholes . . . [namely] *system*"; (2) The main characteristics of such a logic are: (a) that unlike a *relation* (which can always be reduced to two members), a system has an unspecified number of members whose relationships cannot be ordered in linear fashion. This, already goes so far as to call for a reconsideration of our traditional notion of *system*, which we have understood as being "any aggregate of elements, considered together with the relationships holding among them." What we need, therefore, to introduce into the discourse is the notion of *"holistic system."* In such a system, parts do not interconnect "by means of their inherent qualities, but by means of their position in the system. The formation of whole is, consequently, not additional to the aggregation of parts, but

*I am referring particularly to O. Lange, *Wholes and Parts: A General Theory of System Behavior*, Pergamon, 1965; and to various works of Greniewski in the field of the design of cybernetic systems.

[1]*Foundations for a Science of Personality*, Harvard University Press, Cambridge, 1941 (Chapter VIII). Excerpts of this chapter also appear in F. E. Emery (ed.), *Systems Thinking*, Penguin Books, England, 1969.

The reader is also invited to study the above author's more recent work, in which the theme of the need for a logic of wholes is further developed. See, A. Angyal, *Neurosis and Treatment*, Wiley, Glencoe, 1965.

something of an entirely different order." Thus, *"in aggregates it is significant that the parts are added; in a system it is significant that the parts are arranged."* Moreover, ". . . the type of connexions in a whole is very different from the connexions that exist in an aggregate . . . In a holistic system . . . we abstract *constituents* ('elements') and refer only to the *organization* of the whole"; (b) that, traditionally, any relation possesses an "aspect" out of which the relationship is formed, and that such an aspect is an inherent or immanent quality of the object's identity, diversity, similarity, etc. In holistic systems, however, the "members do not become constituents of a system by means of their immanent qualities, but by means of their distribution or arrangement within the system." Hence, such a system exists by virtue of its members' *"positional value";* (c) that relationships, again in traditional logic, exist on the presupposition that the related objects are separate or individuated: hence, they exist in a *"dimensional domain."* This is also true for members of whole systems. But "the role of a dimensional domain in a relationship is merely disjunction of the relata." Whereas, in the formation of systems, the "dimensional domain not only separates the parts, but participates in the formation of the system"; (d) in relationships, "connectedness between relata is a *direct* one." Whereas, "in a system, the members are, from the holistic viewpoint, not significantly connected with each other except with reference to the whole"; (e) it appears, therefore, that the logic of relationships and the logic of systems are probably two different types of logic. Because systems cannot be derived from relations, whereas relations can be derived from systems, the latter must be the more general genus, and the former must merely represent a simplified system, "adequate only for the logical presentation of very simple specialized constellations."*

---

* All italics pertaining to the quotations are in the original text.

In brief, holistic logic calls for the introduction into the discourse of: (i) an unspecified number of components that cannot be analyzed, through arbitrary reductions, into pairs of relata—a point that reveals an entirely new idea of *organization* with regard to systems; (ii) the notion of the positional value of a system's members—a point that gives us a new perspective of the *integration* of system members in a time-sensitive (dynamic) environment; (iii) the notion that "a system is a distribution of the members in a dimensional domain"—a point confirming our initial idea that *environment or situation, as a space-time continuum of events,* determines the action system and is determined by it; (iv) the idea that, in systems, connectedness of members is significant only with reference to the whole—a point that does away with the old notion of causation, which required the finding of a necessary connexion between pairs of facts, and replaces it with the idea of finding the *superordinate system* in which members are connected, or relative to which members have positional value.*

If we now translate this outline of logical requirements in terms of our idea of planning, we find that:

1. Planning defines, or should define, a decision process which organizes human action with respect to some whole system of events that, in our time, is generally a large system.

We can elaborate this statement by reminding ourselves that what we have called situation is an embedding system, which in its totality tends towards de-organization if no organizing and controlling agent operates over its whole space. Human action becomes such a controlling agent when it is planned. Hence it is through planned human action that the situation is organized and controlled. What must

* On this important point, see also Paul Weiss, "Depolarisation: Pointers to Conceptual Disarmament," *Studium Generale*, Vol. 23, Fasc. 10, 1970—especially the section called 'Causality' (pp. 926-932).

be stressed here is that planning organizes and regulates *human action*, and not the environment or the situation.

To be able to regulate human action which, being individually motivated, expresses an immense multiplicity of objectives and goals that are often in conflict with each other, planning itself must be so conceived and organized that the "variety of disturbances" it creates (in the situation) are diminished, and thereby brought under control. At the level of the plan's organization, one way of doing this is to integrate the alternative long-range consequences of action with relation to a generalized "value base" that has relevance to the entire human situation. In the light of such a value base, the notions of "the good" and "the bad" become globalized and, therefore, less sensitive to individual or sectoral interpretations.

This requirement, among others, demands a thorough reconsideration of our current practices of planning, and the introduction of a system-level that we have called "normative planning."

The operational modalities of normative planning have not yet been worked out in detail; consequently, we find here a potential field for intensive effort and research—a field that appears very promising as well as interesting. It confronts us with the need to develop methods that will enable us to visualize, describe and analyse the wide spectrum of alternative consequences that may derive from the decisions and actions which particular goals dictate. Such decisions and actions, as well as such goals (preferred short-range outcomes) must, normatively speaking, be considered within the framework of some whole situation that pertains at a particular time, and be judged with reference to value-sensitive, or value-derived, standards—namely, "norms." These few points should suffice to indicate that our initial efforts in this field must primarily be directed towards very fundamental epistemological questions concerning the role and the nature of values, of value judgments, and of valuation. Such questions have long been neglected in scientific discourse, but the problems that are confronting us suggest that they must be reintroduced into it.*

From such new epistemological findings we can then derive those regularian principles that will render normative planning operational, and permit human action to be so organized, that the variety of disturbances in the situation may be diminished. However, aside from this very major point there is another one in which further research and effort is needed. This other point concerns the idea of "integration," which in current planning remains extremely hazy. Here we come to our second general statement.

   2. Planning must organize human action so that the latter integrates sets of events with reference to their positional value within the space-time continuum of the situation.

We can elaborate this second statement by remembering that *integration* refers to those interactions that create fundamental structures (e.g., in physics and biology, the evolutionary interactivity of certain kinds of phenomena that lead to some perceivable order; in the field of social experience, the mechanisms of association that become manifest as a result of purpose, will, and action—groups, cities, nations, enterprises, etc.).

In the preceding sections of this paper we have seen, that until now our attempts at integrating events through planned action, have remained at the level of, and been governed by, individual rationality—an endeavor that we have always expected, by extension and accretion, to add up to a generalized rationality. Only today, have we come to realize that this is not possible, since extension, accretion and addition are not operations that are relevant to whole

* For a more complete exploration of this question, see Hasan Ozbekhan, *Op. Cit.*

systems, and whole systems define the situations through which we must live. New ways of "arranging" our vision of the situation's member-events has, therefore, become a fundamental requirement of planning.

In order to develop new ideas of what these ways might be, we must reconsider our assumptions about the *nature* of interaction, namely, of the structuring mechanisms that lead to integration.

For our purposes, the basic elements of interaction can be reduced to four major and general couplings:

a. Action-Reaction
b. Equilibrium-Disequilibrium
c. Flexibility-Rigidity
d. Stability-Instability

It is not my intention here to discuss these elements *per se*, but to examine them briefly in relation to the integrative characteristics of planning.* It will be seen that as soon as we do this, the question of the values underlying our deep-seated intellectual habits instantly re-introduces itself into the discussion. There are two levels to the argument insofar as I am able to determine.

On the first level we can establish, that for very old historical reasons, most of humanity—if not all of it—is committed to the belief that order is good, whereas disorder is bad. Whether this fundamental value-judgment happens to be inherently correct or not is not part of our subject, especially since we have defined planning as an order-creating or, at least, as an order-increasing human action model.

The great problems that confront us occur at the second level of the argument. At this level we have traditionally interpreted the good-bad, order-disorder issue in the light of the following assumptions:

* For a very complete discussion of the subject of dynamic inter-action, see, J. Feibleman and J. W. Friend "The Structure and Function of Organization," *Philosophical Review*, Vol. 54, 1945, pp. 19-44.

a. that because action (especially creative action) brings about changes that are not automatically predictable, our planning must be, and is, of the reactive type

a.1 this orthodox view often ignores the fact that reaction:

(i) is a slow adaptive mechanism; (ii) is also a form of action in the sense that it creates new events and change; (iii) is, therefore, a disorder-causing agent, while being, at the same time, an inefficient way of coping with such disorder

b. that because disequilibrium is popularly taken to be synonymous with disorder, our planning has tended to perpetuate division (sectionalism) by holding fast to those areas in which limited equilibria had been attained

b.1 this effort ignores that:

(i) in open systems, such as human action systems, equilibrium often corresponds to stagnation, and stagnation to an increase in de-organization; (ii) in whole systems, partial equilibria do not represent an optimal organization of the whole; (iii) therefore, our commitment to equilibrium *per se* can only be achieved because there are other, vast parts of the system that are disequilibrated, and whose resources we draw upon to keep our so-called equilibrium going, at the expense of suboptimizing the total behavior of the whole system

c. that because flexibility would bring about changes both in our traditional view of planning (a) and in our mode of planning (b), we have conceived all of our institutions and institutional processes in ways that are rigid

c.1 this conception, along with the fear of change it implies, ignores the fact that rigidity:

(i) slows down adaptation; (ii) makes anticipatory action almost impossible; (iii) fragments the situation and the environment

d. that because of the above (a, b and c), we consider stability to be a manifestation of order in the system, and instability a manifestation of disorder

d.1 this attitude makes us forget that:
(i) the situation changes no matter what we do (or don't do) ; (ii) such changes cannot always be controlled with a view towards attaining stability; (iii) instability can also be conceived as a manifestation of order, in certain circumstances that have a dynamic and evolutionary character.

The foregoing points should indicate that the current assumptions underlying our ideas, endeavors and attitudes vis-à-vis interactions are so conditioned as to inhibit the dynamic integration of the situational system's constituent events. Our assumptions, being largely rooted in a static conception of order, create sub-optimal orderings of parts of the whole system, and increases disorder throughout the system. What is required in modern planning theory is a new conception of order, that is based on the positional value of the fast changing events with which we must cope.

The problem of the positional value of events is undoubtedly one of the most difficult for us to deal with, since it involves nothing less than the creation of a general model of the *problématique* we mentioned a few pages earlier. We do not yet know how to build such a model, although we do know that it cannot be based on a traditional consideration of the nature of component problems. In constructing this kind of model we cannot, for instance, say that fluctuations in the price of wheat throughout the world is an economic problem, and approach it as if it were amenable to purely economic solutions, any more than we can summarily dismiss the Negro problem in the United States as a typical minority problem (if such a thing exists). What has to be determined in such a model are the problem-interstices or congruences that create new, unnamed problem-clusters and dynamics. These are the areas of integration of the general *problématique,* and they must be controlled and regulated through planning.

> 3. Such integration must create a dimensional domain, within which events are not only identified as discrete and distinguishable members of the situation, but also as a space-time continuum, that forms a system that is intrinsic to the environment.

One might elaborate this third statement by recalling that "a system is a distribution of members in a dimensional domain."[1] A dimensional domain can be defined with reference to space and with reference to time, making it possible to visualize a multiplicity of objects positioned within their frame. The arrangement of these objects (events, etc.) refers to their positioning, either along a time axis or within a bounded space. When we talk of a space-time continuum, we talk about such an arrangement in both dimensions.

This kind of positioning usually appears to us as pre-structured, which means that we do not recognize the role of human action in the whole system's organization. Planning, however, demands our recognition that we can (and must) arrange members of a system—not only to understand a situation's inner spatial relationships, but also its temporal evolution. Only by doing this can we create alternative configurations of preferred outcomes and of consequences. In other words we can manipulate the system experimentally, and thus conceive ordered approximations of optimal situations.

It is, for instance, through such procedures that we design systems, or space-time orderings of events, which correspond to situations that we want to see crystallize. It is also by such procedures that we diagnose system behavior as "variety-increasing" or "variety-decreasing."[1]

---

[1] A. Angyal, *Op. Cit.*

[1] R. L. Ackoff, *Op. Cit.*

Variety-increasing systems display a higher level of behavior than any of their elements. Variety-decreasing systems operate at a lower level than at least some of their
elements. In every other case, the system elements are
redundant, and their relationships irrelevant. It is a strange
fact that in our day, impressions to the contrary notwithstanding, our planning is generally of the variety-decreasing kind, or it is equilibrated, and suffers from great
redundancies.

How can such a statement be justified with reference to
the current situation which looks so dynamic and seemingly
generates so much variety? The answer and the statement's
confirmation are easy enough to discover if we truly view
the situation as a whole. For, what we take to be variety-increasing behavior occurs mainly in the technological fields,
and is mostly what we called "copying" activity. As such,
it leads to redundancy, and should, therefore, be regarded
as a whole organization in a state of equilibrium. And current, or orthodox, planning is aimed at maintaining such a
state. To grasp the real meaning of this fact, let us remind
ourselves that any system in, or tending towards, equilibrium is one of increasing de-organization, i.e. increasing
disorder (again, if the *whole* is considered). Thus we find
ourselves in the curious circumstance that planning, which
is supposed to be a disorder-reducing process, now tends to
increase disorder.

At this juncture we come face to face with one of the
fundamental points concerning planning, or planned action:
it must be variety-of-disturbance decreasing, and variety-
of-outcome increasing. In other words, plans must be so
conceived that they operate through a minimum of control
and with a maximum of freedom, insofar as the outcomes to
be achieved by means of human action are concerned.

Seen through the optic of our traditional logic, this requirement appears like a paradox that our minds cannot
accommodate. Perhaps a deeper, or at least a different,

understanding of the notion of causality—which means a new perception of reality—will help us to comprehend it.

    4. The causal relationships among events within a dimensional domain need not, in terms of planning, be seen as linear, coupled relationships, but should be understood relative to the entire system of events being visualized or dealt with—namely, to the situational model thus created.

We can elaborate this final statement by remembering that the integration of a situational system is based on events whose causal relationships cannot, ultimately, be determined. The connectedness of the members in such a system has significance only insofar as the members are related to a superordinate system, namely, to a plan. And it is in the hierarchical structuring of the plan that the situation becomes organized, hence meaningful. Its meaning derives from the positional value that the plan—that is, the model of the whole situation—ascribes to events, in the form of ends (values), objectives, goals, and the latter's consequences. This indicates that, in planning, the notion of causality is not rejected, but is viewed as arising from perception of reality and purpose (will), rather than as embodied in the events themselves. By means of such an approach we are enabled to conceive, or talk about, the rationality of the whole as opposed to the rationality of the parts. And the organization of such rationality cannot, insofar as we know today, but proceed from a strict ordering of human action—an ordering that begins from value judgments concerning consequences (ends/objectives), and works backward in time to decisions concerning goals and, finally, means. In other words, starting from a normative level, we move down along the planning system's hierarchical structure to strategies, and ultimately, to operations.

Every point that has been made in this paper supports the need for a logic whose fundamental nature is integrative in terms of causality rather than in linear extension. This kind of logic could also define those mechanisms of integration that would diminish the variety of disturbances to be regulated against—which, as we have seen, is a crucial factor in the conception of *whole* planning systems.

It is obvious that only from the perspective afforded by such a new logical foundation, can one visualize the total structure of an action system, both in its spatial and in its temporal dimensions, with all the components of action and decision *organized*, from perception of reality to consequence —and organized in such a way that the structure of the system as a whole operates simultaneously as a control (or regularian) entity, and as a variety-increasing system.

Nonetheless, we must also recognize that a logic by itself can only help us to discover and manipulate new dimensions of reality; it cannot provide us with the substance of that reality. Its substance must be defined *a priori,* in terms of a generalized value framework. Such a definition constitutes the second integrative — variety-of-disturbance reducing — element that can reinforce the regulation of the whole system without causing the system to sub-optimize the processes it controls, namely, without forcing us to return to a variety-of-outcome reducing system. Furthermore, such a definition can infuse our current notions of ends, and therefore of consequences, with new meaning. It would help yield a consequence-controlling system.

The overall organization of this kind of system corresponds exactly to the hierarchical structure of planning that we have elaborated in the preceding section. At the level of the normative plan and within the frame of a large-scale dimensional system, alternative values, ends, and consequences would be defined and chosen; whereas the strategies and operational decisions would operate, from their respective levels, as instrumental systems within the planned decision process. To repeat, such an organization would integrate the policy and planning functions which, today, represent separate (and divisive) decision processes.

The question will now be asked: How, in such a planning system, does one foresee a consequence? The answer to this question must be that one does *not* "foresee" consequences, but that one chooses from among the alternative consequences one has been able to imagine and verbalize, and one acts so as to cause those chosen consequences to happen, while preventing the discarded consequences from happening.

This is tantamount to saying that in such a system one has to choose the problems one wants to face, and by so doing, one preempts the occurrence-space — seals it off from those problems one does not want, eventually, to be faced with. It is in this sense that the future can be *willed*, and large systems regulated with a minimum of control.

B. Hypotheses and Final Remarks

In this very last part of our essay I shall try, with the utmost brevity, to review what I have attempted to say, and also to propose certain hypotheses concerning planning. This review will not necessarily follow the chronology of the reasoning we have adopted, but I hope that the trend of the reasoning will be recognized.

The hypotheses that emerge from the points we have made can be listed as follows:

1. *Planning and Human Action.*

1.1 Planning is the multi-phased decision structure that underlies all rational human action.

1.2 The function of planning is to integrate human action in terms of given values (ends) and a given perception of reality.

1.3 Another function of planning is to direct human action toward the attainment of pre-visualized, preferred, short-range goals, and toward pre-visualized, preferred, long-range objectives, both of which are outcomes of action.

1.4   Still another function of planning is to visualize goals with reference to objectives, and objectives with reference to consequences.

1.5   Therefore, planning is a decision system that integrates human action in such a way that consequences judged as good will define objectives that are desired and goals that are preferred.

2.   *Planning and Environment.*

2.1   Through planning, man always acts on some object that is extrinsic to the action system, and thereby creates an event which changes his reality-context, namely, his environment.

2.2   Since planning is a decision system that underlies rational action, it defines the purpose of the action.

2.3   The purpose of planned action is to effect changes in the environment so that action will have, as its long-term consequence, changes that are favorable to man—that is, changes which, according to his values, man deems desirable and preferable.

2.4   Changes that are desirable and preferable are those that increase order in the environment and decrease disorder.

2.5   To increase order in the environment, man has to control the environment, by organizing the events that make up the situation which man perceives as his context.

2.6   In our day such events are predominantly man-made rather than "natural"—hence, planning is mainly directed toward the control and rational organization of man-made events.

2.7   Man-made events result from individual plans and actions.

2.8 Therefore, planning must now be viewed as a higher-level organization and integration of individual planned actions.

2.9 This does not mean an increase of control over individuals, but control over the variety of disturbances that individual action creates within the whole situational system.

2.10 Planning must, therefore, determine what these disturbances are, and must decrease their variety.

2.11 To do this, planning must proceed from a new conception of "order."

3. *Planning as a System of Action.*

3.1 A new conception of order requires that planning be conceived as a creative system of human action.

3.2 A creative system of human action is a system that controls processes in which the information required by man to act in the present, is contained in the long-term consequences of action, rather than in short-term known results.

3.3 Such a new conception of planning is, therefore, primarily predicated not on goals (preferred immediate outcomes), which are usually dictated by available means (feasibility), but on ends.

3.4 Ends cannot be cognized with reference to facts; they can only be cognized with reference to values.

3.5 When creative human action is undertaken in accord with shared values, disturbance in the overall situation (environment) is diminished, because the coordination of individual actions can be achieved without the arbitrary restriction of individual freedom, and without rendering the system rigid.

3.6   Values, namely, that which defines "the good," hence "the desirable" and "the preferred" are not static; they change when the situation changes as a result of human action.

3.7   Planning, therefore, must be conceived as a system, that has a "normative" level, which interprets values in the light of the situation, and defines a generalized value base. It is from such a superordinate normative level that the other levels—strategic and operational—of the planning system must be determined. Such a system is hierarchical in nature. It is a hierarchial system of human action.

*   *   *

The foregoing hypotheses do, I believe, cover most of the major points I have tried to bring together in this essay. It is important to bear in mind that they are hypotheses, namely thoughts, that the discourse, approached in the particular manner we have approached it, suggested. They have to be refined, explicated, verified, and doubtless altered. The main lessons we can draw from them at this juncture are: (i) that systems thinking would appear to be a rich and interesting methodology for planning in our day; (ii) that further work along the lines indicated here could conceivably lead us to a general theory of planning, which might possibly enlarge our vision of the social sciences as a whole; (iii) that, at present, our situation is analogous to that of Early Man, our first actor in the examples that we chose, and that we must—as he did—have the courage to pick up the "stone," although we are not quite sure what to do with it.

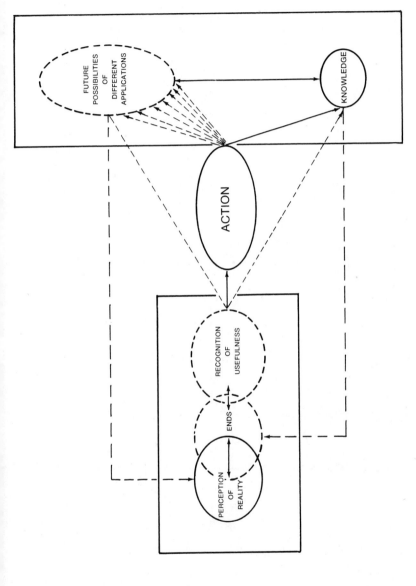

FIG. 1

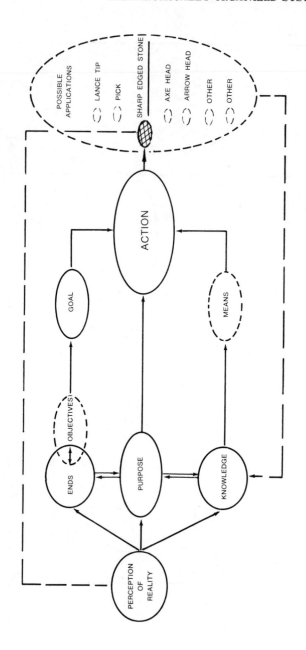

FIG. 2

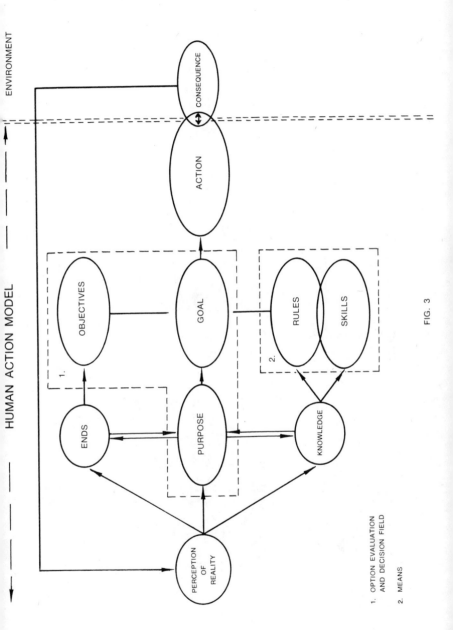

HUMAN ACTION MODEL

ENVIRONMENT

1. OPTION EVALUATION
   AND DECISION FIELD

2. MEANS

FIG. 3

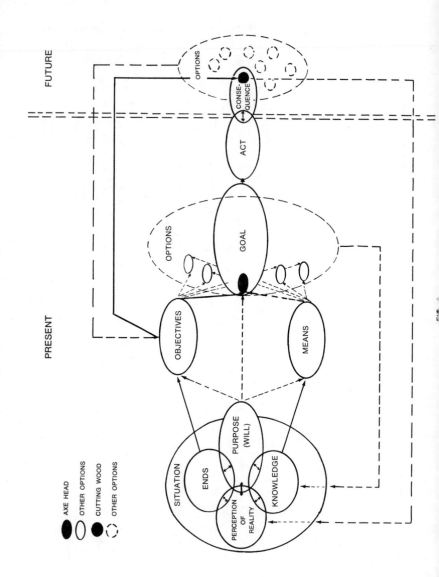

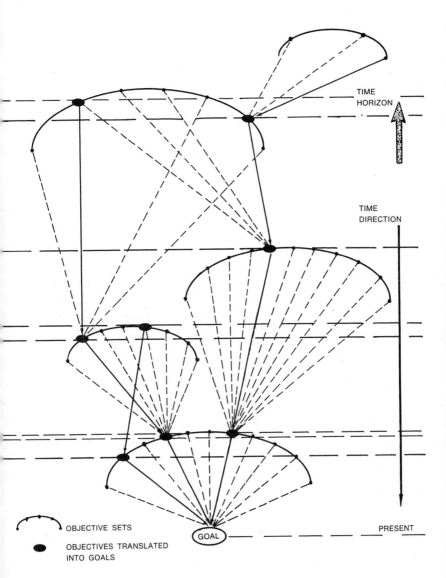

TIME
HORIZON

TIME
DIRECTION

PRESENT

OBJECTIVE SETS

OBJECTIVES TRANSLATED
INTO GOALS

GOAL

FIG. 5

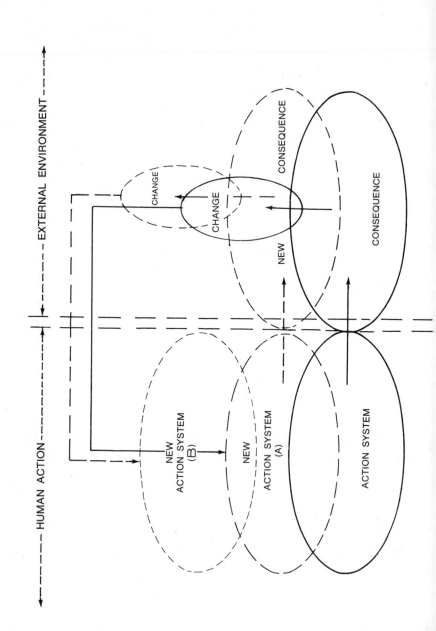

TIME

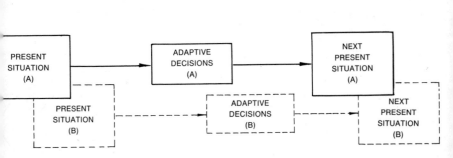

FIG. 7

TIME

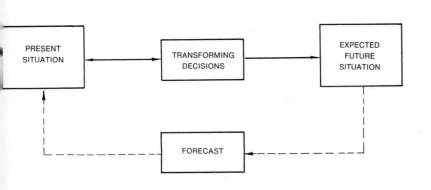

FIG. 8

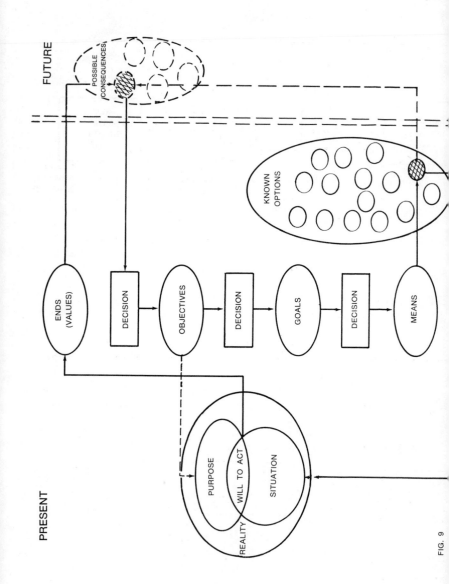

FIG. 9

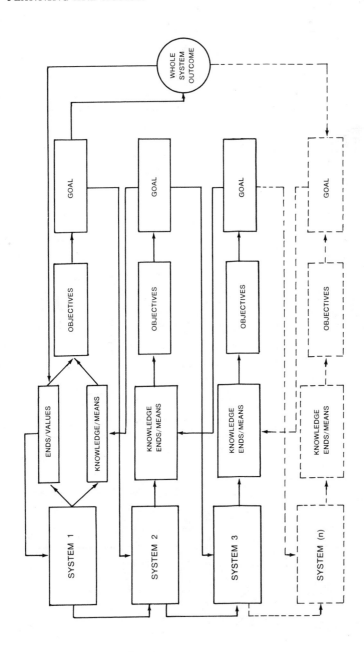

FIG. 10

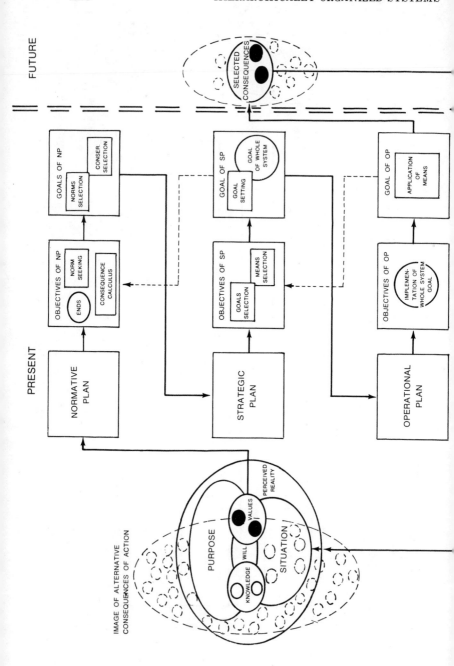

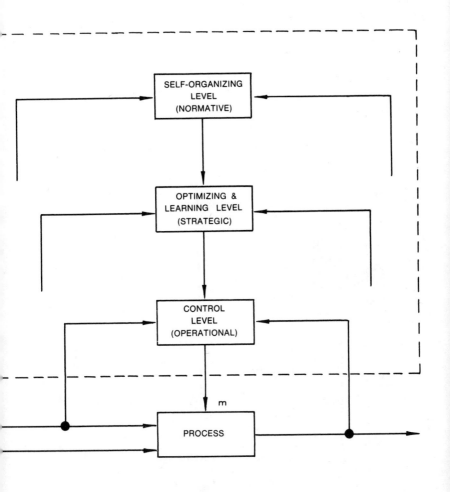

FIG. 12

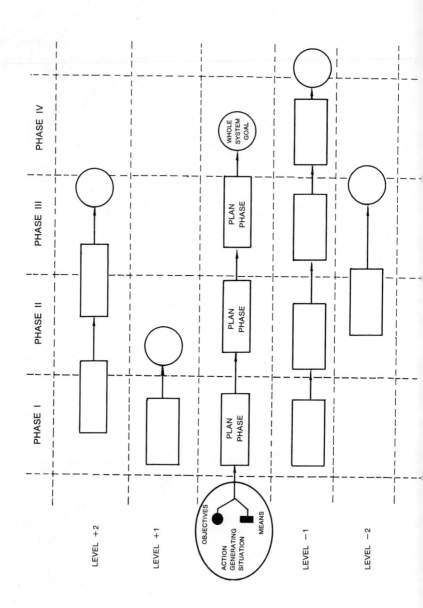

Knowledge, Beliefs and Freedom

Chicago, 8th Jan. 1970 Loyola Centennial

KONRAD LORENZ
*Max-Planck-Institute for Physiology of Behavior,
Seewiesen, Germany*

I. INTRODUCTION

Life in itself is a knowledge process. Human knowledge, personal, cultural and scientific, represents but a special case of a principle by which organic life performs the miracle of developing, in seeming defiance of all laws of probability, in the direction from the less orderly and more probable towards higher harmonies of almost immeasurable improbability. However, there *are* no miracles and in particular there are no infractions on the second law of thermodynamics. Life performs its apparently miraculous creative activity by virtue of a process which is generally called *adaptation* and which is invariably based on feeding *information* into the organic system, information which concerns particular items of its environment relevant to its survival, and which is subsequently retained by the genome.

The information of which I am speaking is not information in the sense of information theory. The latter is intentionally abstracting from the semantic level and from that of survival value. Both, however, are inherent to the concept which common parlance associates with the word information, and which is practically identical with that of *knowledge*. To define this concept in the terminology of information theorists, one may say that an adaptive, or cognitive, process is one by which the organism increases the transinformation existing between itself and its environment in such a way as to increase its chances of survival. All cognitive processes result in constructing, within the living system, an *image* of the particular environment to which it is adapting. The locomotor organs and movements of a fish, for instance, represent an image of the water and of the physics of its wave formation, matching these in all essential details, such as wave length, frequency and amplitude.

Thanks to some very old and abundantly verified theories of Charles Darwin and also to some very new and amazing developments of biochemistry, we have a pretty good idea of the natural processes which achieve the apparent miracle of cognitive adaptation. Modern, biologically-minded epistemologists, like Karl Popper and Donald Campbell have been quick to realize, that the phylogentic process by which a species achieves an increment of knowledge, can be regarded not only as a paradigm, but as the prototype of *all* epistemic activities, such as learning, thought and science. In my contribution to Karl H. Pribram's book ON THE BIOLOGY OF LEARNING, I have tried to demonstrate the common principles that can be generalized to *all* cognitive processes.

In the present paper, my main concern will be with *two* of these general principles which, at a first glance, seem to be irreconcilable antagonists, and yet are both equally indispensable for the continued existence of any living system, as it is upon the equilibrium of these two that survival depends. The first of these principles is *structure* and the second is *freedom*. The first is that of *retention* of knowledge already acquired, the second is that of the *acquisition* of additional knowledge. All adapted structure represents knowledge and all retainable knowledge is laid down in structure. Structure of the chain molecule containing the reproducible knowledge of how to build an organism is at the basis of all life, even of the borrowed life of virus. Yet no increment of knowledge, no improvement of adaptedness can be achieved without dismantling structure, without forgetting what one thought one knew.

Conversely, every structure and the support it offers must be paid for by a corresponding loss of certain specific degrees of freedom. The amoeba can sprout a pseudopod at every point of its body at which it is opportune to do so, the worm can bend wherever it wants to, while any animal with a skeleton can only bend where phylogeny provided a joint. Jakob von Uexküll once wisely said that an amoeba is less of a machine than a horse. Yet the horse is a higher animal than an amoeba and I confidently assert that Johann Sebastian Bach is a higher musician than anyone who thinks he can produce music free from the rigid structure imposed by old laws developed in the course of cultural history.

Throughout the world of organisms it is very obvious that a viable balance is being maintained between the necessary retention of old structure on the one hand, and its partial dismantling necessitated by the changes of environment on the other. As regards the cognitive mechanism of the genome, the stability of genetic retention within a species is clearly correlated with that of its environment. It can be shown that organisms living in the sea, the most unchangeable habitat on earth, are in possession of special buffer mechanisms which exert, even within the genome itself, a selection pressure against all variation of genotype. Conversely, organisms living in a distinctly unstable environment very often possess a phenotype more constant than is the underlying, highly heterozygous genotype which enables the species to respond to newly arising selection pressures by changes in the phenotype without having to "wait" for the occurrence of mutations or recombinations of genes.

II. COGNITIVE PROCESSES IN NON-HUMAN ORGANISMS

a. Homoeostasis

In the paper already mentioned I have tried to explain the fundamental difference between those mechanisms which acquire, and those which retain, knowledge. There are a very great number of physiological processes by which an organism can gain instant information concerning certain quickly variable factors in its environment which require equally instant adaptive measures. The simplest and ubiquitous "invention" of this kind is homoeostasis or the negative feedback cycle. It is hard even to conceive a thought model of a self-perpetuating system without making use of such a cycle. Gerhard Schramm, in his paper on the theoretical pre-requisites of organic life, considers homoeostasis as no less indispensable to life than the coding of information in the chain molecule. The limitation inherent to the latter as a cognitive mechanism lies in the comparatively long period of time which has to pass before the "answer" to any genetic "experiment" is received by the genome of the species. The assumption that this tardy cognitive process should be in itself sufficient to sustain life would only be possible by assuming, at the same time, a constancy and stability of environment which are wellnigh impossible.

The regulating cycle is only one of many means by which the organism is rendered capable of coping with the innumerable short-notice exigencies of its environment. Kineses, phobic responses, taxes and very many other physiological mechanisms described in the paper mentioned above, all serve to feed into the organism instant information concerning sudden environmental changes which need its equally instant attention. All of these mechanisms thus *acquire* knowledge, none of them *retains* it. They *must* not, for the simple reason that they must retain unchanged their readiness to respond to further shifts in the environmental conditions which may well go in the opposite direction. It is, therefore, essential for the function of all these mechanisms that their machinery be not changed by functioning.

b. Modification and true learning

Processes in which the newly acquired knowledge is also

retained, must necessarily effect a change in the machinery of the organism's responses, in other words adaptive *modifications* of this machinery. They are of an entirely different order. Psychologists who are not familiar with evolutionary considerations often have a dangerous tendency to take it for granted that all modification of behavior must be adaptive. The chances of random modification being so is, of course, by no means greater than those of random mutation or recombination of genes. Whenever modification proves to be regularly adaptive to whatever causes it, we are confronted with the certainty that this particular modifiability is caused by having been selected for in phylogeny, in other words, that modification itself is the function of a phylogenetically built-in mechanism.

Such a modifiable behavior mechanism, an *open program,* as Ernst Mayr calls it, pre-supposes not less, but much *more phylogenetically acquired knowledge* than does the "closed" program of rigidly innate, unmodifiable activities. Hence it is not surprising that adaptive modification of behavior does not occur, to any appreciable degree, in organisms not possessing a well centralized nervous system.

The simplest forms of adaptive modification of behavior, like sensitization and desensitization, as well as the simplest forms of association, are occasionally found in lower organisms, but true learning by success and failure definitely is not. It clearly has, for its prerequisite, a rather complicated neuro-sensory mechanism which not only must be able to distinguish, on the basis of built-in phylogenetically acquired knowledge, what is a success and what a failure, but also to feed back, on the mechanisms of temporally preceding behavior, a reinforcing or extinguishing report on the ultimate effect of the behavior chain which the organism has just performed. Even a very cursory consideration of the minimum complication which a neuro-sensory apparatus must possess in order to accomplish this, shows how utterly untenable the assumption is that learning is possible at all levels of animal evolution. On the other hand, above a certain level of neural and sensory integration, all animal phyla, however different, have independently of each other, "invented" this highly efficient and adaptively modifying feed-back to success and failure.

Thus it was at a rather high level of evolution that the genome's function of not only acquiring, but also retaining knowledge, was joined by another mechanism which, at least within narrow temporal limits, could do the same. The amount of knowledge which the genome is able to acquire and to store, is practically unlimited. The human genome contains the coded knowledge how to build a man and a human brain and this by far exceeds all the knowledge stored in all the libraries of all the world. The genome, however, needs time periods of a size order of geological epochs to acquire that knowledge, in fact it needs the duration of several generations to acquire any knowledge at all. Learning, on the other hand, is only able to retain a comparatively infinitesimal quantity of knowledge, and is furthermore only able to do so for an extremely short period, for the life-span of the individual at the best, *but* it is able to acquire *and* retain knowledge almost at a moment's notice. Even unaided by other functions, learning develops an enormous survival value, as is witnessed by its omnipresence in higher animals of all phyla.

Even in some birds and mammals, the mechanism of learning by failure and success cooperates, in a more highly integrated function, with two other cognitive functions. The first is a newly arising appetite for learning, so-called curiosity, leading to a latent hoard of potentially useful knowledge which is, in a sense, objective, very much like the "scientific" knowledge of man. The second is the social function of handing down, from one generation to the next, individually acquired knowledge. Together the two processes achieve the effect of acquiring knowledge and retaining it over a period exceeding the life span of an individual.

III. CUMULATING TRADITION AND CULTURE

In our own species, a curious little feedback in the first of these two functions causes them to be welded into a super-imposed system of much higher integration, and of truly epoch-making new systemic properties. The "little" addition is conceptual thought. A creature in which exploratory behavior has reached extreme degrees of importance, could not fail, sooner or later, to include its own self in the wide circle of subject-matters to be explored: thus arose *reflexion*. Reflexion entails a new level of *objectivation*. To see my grasping hand at work, and to realize that it is just as much an object of outer reality as the object which I see it grasping, is probably the first of the cognitive functions which extract the concept of an object out of its particular form of graspability. The inclusion of ourselves in a world thus conceived made it possible for us to abstract, also, from our present physiological state: being fully fed, we should be essentially disinterested in a piece of bread, but knowing ourselves as we do, we take it with us to appease future hunger.

All this is present in anthropoids, to a greater degree than was assumed a short time ago. But it is only in man that conceptual thought, united with tradition, made it possible to accumulate supra-individual knowledge over periods of time and in quantities that seem unlimited in principle. This accumulating tradition is *culture*. It is nothing miraculous, nothing beyond the scope of the science of biology, but it is *biologically* more unique and more wonderful than is ever realized by those who are most desperately anxious to show that man is different in kind, and not only in degree, from all other animals and that the laws of nature applying to them do not apply to him.

It is quite possible that conceptual thought only reached higher differentiation when it became integrated with tradition. Certainly it was this integration which made syntactic language possible. Syntactic language is itself a product of an *accumulation* of traditional knowledge. On the other hand, any higher degree of traditional knowledge must obviously, from the first, have been the prerequisite of language. Both must have developed hand in hand; which came first is a hen-and-egg problem. But the integration of conceptual thinking and tradition must indeed have occurred to begin with.

However it may have originated, cumulative tradition is a cognitive mechanism entirely unprecedented in the history of life. For many millions of years its continuity was based on the continuity of the knowledge handed down, from one generation to the next, by the reduplication of the chain-molecules. Individual immortality of knowledge rested exclusively on the potential immortality of the germ plasm. Barring a small amount of non-cumulative tradition in the very highest vertebrates, this state of affairs prevailed unchanged throughout the evolution of the organic world, from virus-like forms of pre-life up to the anthropoids.

The constant harping on the spiritual uniqueness of man tends to obscure his biological uniqueness. Cumulative tradition endows man with neither more nor less than the faculty to inherit acquired characters, a faculty non-existent in any other species. If a man invents a tool, for instance bow and arrows, not only his progeny, but all his culture will henceforth possess these aids to survival; the likelihood of their ever being forgotten is no greater than that of a bodily organ of equal survival value becoming vestigial. Thus, cumulative tradition engenders a continuity not only of knowledge, but also of aims, which outlive the individual and can endure and go on growing for ages. It is an altogether new kind of potential immortality, one in which the individual plays an incomparably more decisive role than it does in the anonymous continuity of the germ plasm.

A yarn of ever-increasing volume is being spun both by the knowledge-acquiring and knowledge-preserving procedures within the genome of any species and by those of any culture. While an animal is predominantly the creature of its genome and of its very limited individual experience, man is not only formed by these but additionally by the inheritance of all characters historically acquired by his culture. Man is *by nature* a creature of culture, that is to say he is phylogenetically so programmed as to depend on the existence of a vast hoard of cultural inheritance. His speech centers rely on a culturally developed syntactic language and his huge forebrain has evolved in the service of learning and of teaching the hoard of culturally accumulated wisdom and knowledge.

Deprived of cultural inheritance man would not be a happy savage, as the slogan of Jean Jacques Rousseau "revenez à la nature" implies, but a miserable cripple who could not even speak, comparable to those wretched patients who, as a consequence of severe encephalitis, are deprived of most higher brain functions. It seems to be necessary to emphasize this fact, because there are people like Herbert Marcuse who seriously believe that after the complete destruction of a culture a new and better one must necessarily sprout out of the ruins—which it could never do. Although it is true that in one respect a culture is more difficult to extinguish than the lives of its bearers—as it can survive in libraries and other forms of objectivation—it is on the other hand more vulnerable than the living people who are its members. A culture can easily be destroyed while the peoples who bore it survive. There are many examples of this in the history of our planet's colonization.

It was the great philosopher Nicolai Hartmann, understandably rejected by the majority of typical "Geisteswissenschaftler," who saw with great clarity that all spiritual existence, whether personal, objective or objectivated, has its fundaments in the lower and more general strata of the real world and is dependent on living, sentient organisms much in the same way as the latter are dependent on, and

-still consist of, the same elments of which inorganic matter consists. A "Naturwissenschaft vom menschlichen Geist," any attempt to approach the human spirit in the spirit of research was, and still is, regarded by many German philosophers as an inane, value-blind blasphemy. Still this is exactly what I shall attempt here.

IV. APPROACHING CULTURE AS A LIVING SYSTEM

The uniqueness of human culture is the specific systemic property of a system which, as I have attempted to show, originated from the integration of pre-existing sub-systems, exploratory behavior and tradition, none of which is specifically human and none of which possesses the systemic properties which come into existence by their integration only. No miracle is necessary to explain the creation of the human "Geist." The endeavor to reach a natural, that is to say biological, understanding, so far from constituting a blasphemy, is a real necessity, for the simple reason that, like any other living system, that of human culture is subject to pathological disturbance, to *illness*. In English, one speaks of mental illnesses while in German, characteristically, these are termed "Geisteskrankheiten." This word is contradictory in itself, as it is obviously impossible that something extra-natural and opposite to nature should be subject to physiological malfunctions. However, nobody will deny that our culture is thoroughly sick nowadays, and this alone is sufficient justification for the attempt to analyze it by the methods used to approach living systems in general.

In approaching an un-analyzed living system, the first step must unconditionally consist in the attempt to get a general survey knowledge of the subsystems which, on the highest level of integration, are immediately subordinate to the whole. This principle has been expounded in detail by Paul Weiss, myself and others, so that I can confine myself to essentials here. In the gaining of this first survey knowledge, Gestalt-perception, often called "intuition," or "inspired guess" play a decisive role. Furthermore, pathological disturbance of a sub-system can be a help in drawing attention to its function by demonstrating what happens when it is lacking. Last but not least, functional analogy to other better-known systems can be used as a pointer on how to arrange a first, sketchy and consciously provisional "flow diagram" which provides little more than a memory aid to indicate which and how many independent functions have been observed, what and how many sub-systems must be postulated, and in what direction the stream of energy or information, or both (mostly both) is flowing from one to the other. It needs some methodological sophistication to keep in mind that one "box" of such a diagram represents a function and not a physiological mechanism and to avoid misleading reifications arising from the confusion of these two.

If we try to apply these methods to the study of the system which, in the historical development of a culture, performs the functions of not only acquiring, but also of retaining and storing adaptive knowledge, we can gain valuable help from its obvious analogies to those other organic systems which achieve comparable functions in the development of an individual and of a species. The study of the first, of learning, habit-formation and habit-retention will be important because all these processes enter into and are part of the living system of a culture. On the other hand, the striking analogies between cultural and phylogenetic development are of importance for exactly opposite reasons: the mechanisms achieving each of these two chains of events are of different physiological nature. Therefore, all the far reaching and detailed analogies existing between the results of both can only be explained by identity of function and consequent converging evolution.

In all growth, phylogenetic, ontogenetic and cultural, a dualism of antagonistic functions must achieve a viable equilibrium: acquisition and retention of adaptive knowledge. As I have already explained at the beginning of this paper, adaptive knowledge is always structure and the supporting function of structure must always be paid for by a loss of freedom. New knowledge can be added to old knowledge only to a limited degree, just as a building cannot indefinitely be built upon without changing its underlying structure. In the case of the genome, the acquisition of new knowledge inescapably is identical with the dismantling of something already attained. The opposite, however, is not true by any means, the dismantling of structure as such has but an infinitesimal chance of being adaptive. It is necessary to state this truism, because some people honestly believe that dismantling traditional structures of a culture is identical with progress. Unlike the phylogenetic procedure of the genome, the ontogeny of the individual and the historic development of a culture are both dependent on special, built-in dismantling mechanisms which will have to be discussed later. For the moment, I turn to the description of those functions which acquire cultural knowledge and those which retain it.

V. PROCESSES ACQUIRING CULTURAL KNOWLEDGE

As I have already said, *all* kinds of individually acquired knowledge can, on principle, be retained in tradition. Above, I have chosen an invention, that of a tool, for the example of an acquired character which forthwith became a firm possession of society. When a brain-wave of an individual results in a discovery of equally impressive survival value, it certainly will have permanent effects on a culture, particularly in times like our own, when science stands in high repute and mass media broadcast its findings. As rational beings, we like to think that most of our cultural knowledge and wisdom stems from rational processes in general and from intellectual insight in particular. As a boy, I was taught by a highly erudite and biologically-minded teacher of religion that Moses, when he declared the pig unclean and forbade the consumption of pork, really knew about trichinosis, but considered it more effective to trust his community's religious devotion rather than its medical intelligence. This interpretation is certainly erroneous. Historians can show, beyond reasonable doubt, that the taboo on the pig and some other animals arose in an altogether different manner from purely magical causes. It is, however, an inspired error because it illustrates a really existing principle by an example which does not apply—which has happened in the history of science much more often than one would think.

I venture to suggest that most of the norms of behavior which are handed down by tradition, have developed from fortuitously acquired habits rather than from rational insights, and also that it was the good old process of natural selection which chose the expedient and advisable ones for perpetuation. Habits are formed much more quickly than most people tend to think. As I have already said, a creature possessing little exploratory drive and less causal insight will indeed be well advised to repeat, meticulously, any sort of procedure that has once attained its goal without incurring any offsetting stimulus situations. A greylag goose or a horse, for instance, will stick most tenaciously to a path habit fulfilling these conditions even after having run through it only a single time. Under certain circumstances, people behave in an analogous manner, and, with repetition, become more and more fond of the habit, while, at the same time, any infraction upon it provokes fear, as I shall explain in the next chapter dealing with the retentive mechanisms of cultural tradition. This psychological mechanism forms the basis of that which usually is called"magical thinking" by ethnologists and psychologists.

The course of human ontogeny is phylogenetically so

programmed that the growing child, in the process of its socialization, not only acquires all the habits of the significant persons in its environment, but also internalizes these norms of behavior, that is to say, learns to regard them as values to be cherished. Experts on child behavior tell us that motoric imitation of the action patterns which the child observes in the adults, play an important role in this process. In fact, imitation seems to come first and the understanding for the meaning of the imitated behavior only later on. Extremely sharp powers of observation and a striking gift for imitation are both typical of healthy and active little children. An excellent analysis of the process of primary and secondary socialization and the concomitant internalization of cultural norms is given in Peter Berger's book "The Social Construction of Reality."

There is one strong argument in favor of the assumption that the bulk of rites and norms of social behavior which are handed down by tradition, have their origin in random habit formation—or other random processes—and in the selection of the most expedient. This argument lies in the fact that the historical development of a culture behaves in so very similar a manner as does speciation. Between the phylogenetic events which establish rites and norms of social behavior in a species, and those processes which do the same in the historical development of a culture, there are a number of parallels reaching far beyond the scope of functional analogy. In fact, the identical methods of comparative study are applicable in the endeavor to reconstruct the course they have taken in the history of the world. Tribute is due to Sir Julian Huxley who, as early as 1914, fully appreciated these parallels and coined the term of *ritualization* for both the phylogenetic and the cultural process. Ritualization is a process of acquisition as well as of retention of adaptive knowledge. Its discussion may, therefore, opportunely be placed between the chapters dealing with these two subjects.

VI. RITUALIZATION

Julian Huxley discovered the important fact that many signals which serve social communications within an animal species are derived from motor patterns that originally had evolved in the service of an altogether different survival value. A movement which originally served the building of a nest can develop into a signal communicating the readiness to do so to another individual. At the beginning of this development, the movement in question may still retain its original function, in our example the bird may really work at its nest while the beginning of the new adaptation to a communicative function consists only in increasing and accentuating those parts of the motor pattern which happen to send out the most effective stimulation. This is widely-spread and usually termed "mimic exaggeration." With the further evolution of the signal, the original function may be entirely lost, while the motor pattern may be so changed that its "unritualized model" can hardly be recognized in it any more. Practically all the communication underlying all social collaboration of animals is built up on the basis of this process of ritualization.

The ceremonies which thus arise in phylogeny are not, of course, truly symbolic, but they show amazing parallels to human ceremonies that are. These similarities are, certainly, to a great part, explicable on the basis of functional analogy, but, as I said, they reach a bit further than that. Otto Koenig's recent book on Cultural Ethology contains an extremely thorough study of the historical development of the soldier's uniform. Comparative investigation reveals the existence of many truly vestigial, e.g. entirely functionless characters, as well as true changes of function, strictly comparable to those occurring in the phyletic development of organs. *The course, which development takes, seems to be as blind, as devoid of direction, as that of phylogeny, which seems to indicate that human intelligence and purposive insight play no part in that kind of cultural ritualization.*

There is hardly one among the innumerable learned activities which a human being performs in his or her daily life, that is not, under certain circumstances, handed down to the next generation by a process of teaching by example. In other words, there is hardly one learned action pattern, however practical and adapted to its mechanical function, which does not possess an additional function of *communication*. It is in the service of this communicative function that so many action patterns of man have undergone those characteristic changes which constitute the essence of ritualization. It is hardly an exaggeration to say that every pattern handed down by tradition becomes, with time, endowed with those frills and embellishments which, by making it more impressive, facilitate its handing-down. The apprentice of the ancient smith had to learn that a newly forged sword must be tempered, while still red-hot, in cold water, but if he is taught to do it three times, twice in running water and once in the morning dew, according to the precept of Kipling's Weyland smith of the gods, the procedure is *so* much more impressive and its necessity so much more convincing. And, what is more, that kind of embellishment *may* contain, irrespective of their non-rational origin, some very real improvements which are consequently taken up and reinforced by natural selection. Many good recipes of cooking and many valuable methods of medical treatment originated in that way. For all we know, Weyland's method of tempering may really have some practical advantages, and anyone convinced that pork-eating is a grave sin, will regard it as a just punishment and a visitation of the Gods if, after committing it, his neighbor dies of trichinosis.

For obvious reasons, this mechanism of cultural ritualization, changing and elaborating even at those traditional patterns of behavior that serve man's interaction with his extra-specific environment, attains an incomparably greater scope with all those other behavior patterns which exclusively serve the interaction between fellow-members of human society. The kind and the numbers of the things a man can perform in the forging of a sword, are still determined and limited by what is necessary to produce a good sword in a tolerably short time, but what happens in a purely communicative, intraspecific ceremony is subject to practically no limitation. The kind and number of words used in a polite letter-ending by a Frenchman, the bird-of-paradise feathers worked into the ceremonial headgear of a Papuan warrior, or the number of pettycoats worn by a Slovakian peasant girl or the amount of chromium worn by a big American car, are all calculated to impress a fellow-member of the species who is apt to retaliate in kind, with the result of intra-specific selection leading to extremes.

The wisdom, the adaptive knowledge contained in this kind of intraspecific ritualization is more difficult to disentangle from the purely accidental, and also probably is proportionally smaller than that permeating the ritualized addition to purely technical procedures. Still, even the most abstruse-seeming ritualizations can become indispensable. As I said, the system of traditional norms of behavior, fixated by ritualization, performs a function which, within the living system of a culture, is analogous to that performed by the skeleton within an animal's body. Abolishing one of these rigid customs may be equivalent to the removal of an indispensable support, and cause the collapse of the culture.

In one particular respect, the parallels between phylogenetic and cultural ritualization throw a light on one of humanity's most urgent problems: on war. Erik Erikson showed that culturally ritualized norms of behavior, in becoming more and more different in independently developing cultures, perform a *separating* function, analogous to that which phylogenetically ritualized behavior patterns accomplish as barriers to hybridization. He coined the term "pseudo-speciation" to describe a cultural phenomenon of the utmost importance: pseudo-speciation has the consequence that one culture does not regard the members of another as really and truly human. This weakens the normal inhibitions to kill conspecifics and is one of the prerequisites of war.

VII. PROCESSES RETAINING CULTURAL KNOWLEDGE

Habits are quickly formed and any infraction of habit produces anxiety, not to say *fear*. Whatever the physiological mechanisms of these phenomena are, they form the fundament of all processes serving the preservation of cultural knowledge once attained. In my youth, long before one-way streets existed, I had formed the habit of riding to and from the motorcycle mechanic's shop, which the weaknesses of motor vehicles of that time necessitated, by two entirely different routes of approximately equal length. This path habit originated by pure chance, and when I became conscious of it, I experimentally tried to invert it. The result was as surprising as it was impressive: I experienced an indubitable and amazingly strong onset of anxiety which was so disagreeable that I discontinued the experiment. Comparable examples of animal behavior are well known. My young greylag goose who had formed a detouring path habit and under the stress of extreme hurry went the direct path, became frightened, stopped, returned, ceremoniously performed the detour, then continued her way reassured. Margaret Altmann's mounts, an ancient horse and a still more venerable mule refused to go past a place at which Dr. Altmann had camped a few times, balking with all the symptoms of extreme fear, until, initiated to the intricacies of animal behavior, she performed a cursory symbolic unpacking and repacking, whereupon the animals agreed to go on.

The farther the origin of a custom slides back into the

past, the greater the number of times that it has been transmitted from a father to a son, and the more elaborate have become the ritualized frills it has acquired in the process, the more a true, active *love* for the custom is added, as a factor motivating its continuance, to the persistent fear at any infraction of it. In other words, the traditional norm of behavior *tends to assume many of the emotional values of the father figure* which the adolescent has come to know as its representative and which he both fears and loves. Ultimately, in old and highly developed cultures, the essential qualities of a super-normal father-figure tend to become condensed into a father-god. With that, the infraction of the norm of behavior prescribed by custom comes to be regarded, not only as dangerous, but as outright *immoral*.

As modern people, overrating our own rationality, we often blind ourselves to the fact that *all* habits, even habits of thought and even those of the highest scientific order, unavoidably undergo this kind of cultural development: individual cognitive achievement becomes habit, habit transmitted becomes custom, custom, when continued long enough, becomes religious imperative. As Thomas Huxley said, every truth begins as heresy and ends up as orthodoxy.

As scientists, we may lament this rapid degeneration of newly found scientific truth into orthodox religion, but we must face the fact that the same course of events unavoidably happens with *all* scientific truth. It is beyond the powers of the human mind to keep constantly aware that nothing whatsoever among the many things which we think we know, is ultimate truth. We could not go on building up new theories, new knowledge, on their basis, if we constantly faced the indubitable fact that they all are nothing but crude approximations to extra-subjective reality, to Immanuel Kant's thing in itself, and that, moreover, we are quite unable to guess *how* crude this approximation really is. We *have* to believe that some of our knowledge is "really" true, and we have, as modest and respectful pupils, a certain tendency to believe that all a revered and beloved teacher tells us is rather more true than what we have found out ourselves. This attitude toward a teacher is dangerous to a degree: If pupils turn into disciples, the further accumulation of scientific knowledge is irreparably blocked.

Yet, if I try to face my own scientific convictions with pitiless honesty, I have to confess that there are quite a number of scientific "truths" which I do *not* regard—as in principle I should—as provisional approximations, but as being truly and ultimately true, though, in writing this line I have just caught myself shirking the expression "absolutely true". I am convinced that the earth moves around the sun, that all animals including man are descended from common ancestors, and quite a number of other things. Now, if somebody came along with some perfectly valid scientific arguments contradicting my truth, I am afraid that I should turn a deaf ear to them and find pseudo-rational reasons for not accepting them. If he afforded proof irrefutable, I might possibly flare into religious rage. In other words, *all* cultural knowledge, irrespective of its provenience, takes on all the properties of a magical belief, of a non-rational superstition, after it has been handed down for a few generations.

Nobody is above this kind of reaction which one might term the "magical response." However, if we look it squarely in the face and are honest with ourselves, we might do something rational about it. We must not forget that the magical response is an *indispensable* function without which cultural knowledge and, with it, cultural ethics, would disintegrate completely. However, we must not forget that, as I have said in my book ON AGGRESSION, the same basic factor accounts "for the unfaltering tenacity with which a good man clings to the handed down customs of his culture. His fidelity might seem to be worthy of a better cause, but there *are* a few better courses! If social norms and customs did not develop their own peculiar autonomous life and power, if they were not raised to sacred ends in themselves, there would be no trustworthy communication, no faith and no laws. Oaths cannot bind, nor agreements count, if the partners to them do not have in common a basis of ritualized behavior standards at whose infraction they are overcome by the same magic fear as seized my little greylag on the staircase in Altenberg."

VIII. PROCESSES DISMANTLING CULTURAL KNOWLEDGE

As I explained in the introduction, all knowledge is structured and the adaptedness of structure is equal to knowledge. It is irrelevant whether knowledge is laid down in the structure of chain molecules, of printed books in libraries, of synaptic configurations in a man's brain, or in the traditional ritualizations of a culture. New knowledge can be added to existing knowledge only to a limited degree, just as a building cannot indefinitely be built upon without effecting changes in its basic structure. The growth of a bone is brought about not only by the osteoblasts, which add calcified tissue to the one already existing, but just as much by the osteoclasts, which gnaw away provisional structure to make room for new bone pillars, better suited to support the form of a larger animal. The age old method which the genome uses in gaining new knowledge is based on the same principle: an actual *error* in the transmission of knowledge, a little breaking-down of molecular structure, is indispensable to open the door by which new and better knowledge may attain entrance. My admired teacher Karl Bühler, when speaking of learning in general, used to say aphoristically that one might define that which is learned as that which can be forgotten again. The scientist, in his daily work, makes a most sophisticated use of systematized intentional error, that of the working hypothesis. Piet Hein expresses this ubiquitous method in his wonderful verse:

> The way to wisdom? Why, it's plain,
> And easy to express:
> To err, and err, and err again,
> But less, and less, and less.

The faculty thus to dismantle older beliefs and to gain new knowledge proverbially decreases with age, while the tenacity with which a man adheres to traditional knowledge increases correspondingly. If a society consisted exclusively of elderly die-hards, the plasticity of its cultural norms of behavior would probably not exceed that of instinctual, genetically fixed patterns.

In my paper on THE ENMITY BETWEEN GENERATIONS AND ITS PROBABLE ETHOLOGICAL CAUSES, I have proposed the hypothesis that there exists, in our species, a phylogenetically built-in mechanism which performs, in the development of a culture, a function strictly analogous to that which the osteoclasts perform during the growth of a bone. It is a regular, lawful event in the ontogeny of man to loosen the allegiance to parental tradition, and to cast about for new ideals, for new causes to embrace. Normally, this happens in the early post-puberal years, but the temporal variation seems to be considerable. Under normal and "healthy" circumstances, the adolescent does not jettison *all* the traditions of the culture into which he or she was born. The iconoclast is as indispensable for the adaptive growth of the system of which he forms a part, as the osteoclast is to the growing bone, nor does he, normally, destroy that system: it is only under certain circumstances that something comparable to osteoporosis attacks a culture! In a healthy culture, the adolescent, after having critically sifted the worth and unworth of parental tradition, tends to *take back* more and more of its values as he grows older. Any old man of my age will agree that, at the age of sixty-six, he holds his father in much higher esteem than he did when he was eighteen. Mitscherlich has called this phenomenon "late obedience."

There is no doubt that this "post-puberal moulting of ideals" represents the open door which permits the bulk of the new knowledge which rejuvenates and transforms a culture to gain entrance. It is characteristic of our species that its curiosity and its exploratory behavior does not diminish appreciably with sexual maturity, as it does in most other animals. Arnold Gehlen speaks of "Weltoffenheit," of a permanent ability to adapt to self-made new environment. I myself think that this ability has its very narrow limits and that even within these, man's openness to new environmental situations decreases rapidly with age. Of course, the scientist's frequent exercise of hashing-up cherished hypotheses does have a certain effect of spiritual limbering-up. The cognitive processes characteristic of scientific man, the forming of hypotheses and the matching of their patterns with those of outer reality, and others, are not much damaged until real senility sets in—which it does at very different ages in different individuals.

IX. DISEQUILIBRATION OF RETENTIVE AND DISMANTLING PROCESSES

As have said in the introduction, the survival of any living system, in an environment that is forever changing, more slowly or more quickly, is largely dependent on an equilibrium between knowledge-gaining and knowledge-retaining functions, on a balance which is suited to the rate of environmental change. Too much retention leads, in a changing environment, to maladaptation and sooner or later to extinction, too little retention necessarily leads to that type of monster which can be experimentally produced, in genetic experiments, by artificially increasing the mutation rate of a species, for example by radiation.

Anybody looking at our own culture with the disillusioned

eye of the biologist and the medical man, will sadly agree that it contains an alarming abundance of fossils, as for instance the miraculously surviving right-wing movement in Germany, as well as of wildly formless monsters who believe in the total destruction of tradition, like Herbert Marcuse.

In my paper on the enmity between generations and its probable ethological causes, I have discussed the factors which tend to disrupt the normal and necessary handing-down of cultural knowledge. In the present context, it suffices to say that most of the sociological conditions for successful transference of cultural tradition are rapidly deteriorating: the father is no more a figure to be revered and loved, far less to be feared, and least of all to be identified with, while, on the other hand, all the young of all the world, as an effect of easy transportation and mass media, are becoming more and more similar to each other, and, therefore, find it easier to identify with each other than with the parent generation of their own respective cultures. This literally leads to tribal warfare between the generations: the hate they bear each other is of the nature of national hate. On the other hand, the function of the processes discussed in chapter V., the re-assessment of all traditional values and the search for new ideas, for new causes to embrace, all of which is normally performed by the post-puberal young, becomes more and more difficult to achieve. The rapid change, both ecological and sociological, forced on humanity by the explosive development of technology, necessitates an ever-increasing gap between the norms of social behavior which are sensible and expedient in one generation and those which must be postulated in the next. In other words, the task set to the post-puberal "moult of ideas" becomes more and more difficult, the prerequisites for performing it successfully become more and more deficient while the necessity to do so becomes more and more urgent.

What ails our culture is not, however, a simple upsetting of the balance between retentive and dismantling processes in the favor of the latter. It is not as if the osteoclasts were having a field day with the ossifying agencies completely silenced. The worst kind of ossification is busily proceeding, unnoticed by the rebelling youthful, within their very own ranks.

Two independent tendencies, more or less antagonistic to each other, are to be found in the youthful during their iconoclastic phase. The first is to take an altogether intelligent and highly sceptical attitude towards all traditional truth, the second is to embrace gladly and with a notable lack of scepsis any new truth that happens to be offered. As long as the right equilibrium is maintained between them, these two tendencies form a regulating system. However, young people are impatient, and if their critical reassessment of traditional truths shows up too many of them as obsolete and no longer true, they simply refuse to waste intelligent thought on correcting and adapting tradition, and become surprisingly ready to accept uncritically any new doctrine. As there is a strong urge to *fight* for a cause, any doctrine that is controversial, or in the minority, or for some other reason in need of enthusiastic support, will prove dangerously attractive to the young. In the extreme case of paternal tradition becoming completely inacceptable, a completely uncritical, purely religious acceptance of a new doctrine can *eliminate intelligence and reason* from taking part in the necessary dismantling of traditional knowledge.

X. OSCILLATION OF PUBLIC OPINION

This effect is extremely dangerous. Human reason and intelligence must play the main role in dismantling truth that has become calcified into superstition. If that kind of fossil is broken up, not by intelligent critique, but just by another, opposing doctrine, nothing is gained. Moreover, two orthodoxies standing against each other can give rise to an altogether devastating effect—to *oscillation*, a phenomenon common to very many systems, living and non-living, in which regulation is achieved by counteraction of two factors. The example which obtrudes itself on the ethologist is that of conflicting motivations in any higher animal: at lower levels of intensity, they achieve a regulative, steady balance, but if the specific excitation of both is raised beyond a certain limit of tolerance, the organism breaks out in *alternating* movements, crazily switching to and fro between two incompatible intentions.

Even in technical regulating systems, the oscillation can become self-exciting, with the result that it builds up, in a positive feedback effect, until the whole device fuses or breaks apart. Technicians have coined for this undesirable event the term "regulating catastrophy" (Reglerkatastrophe).

Comparable disequilibrations can afflict a culture when, in the manner just described, reason and intelligence are prevented from participating as controlling factors in the antagonistic, but mutually regulating processes of retaining and dismantling cultural knowledge. As long as these higher cerebral functions retain control, the to-and-fro of public opinion remains a *damped* oscillation. In other words, the *first* wave of emotions is the highest one, after which public opinion vacillates with decreasing amplitude, finally settling at a point which, in the optimal case, is a better approach to truth than the new heresy had ever been. In this manner, the swing of public opinion may be regarded as an altogether desirable scanning mechanism which explores extremes and settles for something quite sensible. Many new scientific findings and their gradual acceptance and digestion by public opinion are examples of this regular sequence of events.

The removal of any dampening factors does not yet make an oscillation self-exciting. To make it so, it is necessary that any displacement in one direction causes another opposite one which *exceeds* it in size.

Several conditions must be fulfilled to bring about this phenomenon. For one thing, there must be a tension between two opposing opinions, each of which errs in the direction of exaggeration, over-simplification and rigid indoctrination, so that the truth actually rests *between* the two extremes. This is the case to which Hegel's great assertion applies that, in regard to any thesis whatsoever, the antithesis is always true.

Secondly, a time-lag must be contained in the system which, in the case of oscillating public opinion is caused by the period necessary to make proselytes, first in one direction, and, after the pendulum has swung the full way, in the other. The time-lag of change in public opinion may coincide with, and certainly always is influenced by the duration of a generation. It is mainly the young who discard orthodoxies, usually dismantling them further than is necessary, and who always are all too prone to go to opposite extremes, thus creating the situation conducive to rebound phenomena.

Thirdly, each of the two opposing opinions must possess a really great number of adherents, as any opinion gains in power to convince with increasing numbers. When, within a population, the density of the followers of a doctrine exceeds a certain value, the unconvinced and the dissenters cease to count and the community of the indoctrinated assumes the character of an ethnic group. The doctrine is then defended with equally militant enthusiasm as are the ethnic symbols of a tribe which make for its cohesion and are its symbols and banners in tribal warfare. In its service of this function as a symbol, the doctrine loses much of its former intellectual properties, it becomes more and more rigid, and, at the same time, more simplified, until it assumes the character of a slogan, easy to remember, easy to hammer in by conditioning, and easy to yell in chorus. The further this process has progressed, the more difficult it becomes to concede that this doctrine is not, after all, the ultimate and absolute truth. It becomes impossible to the indoctrinated to listen and answer intelligently to criticism, and the antagonist therefore, feeling relieved of the duty of offering any, follows his own inclination to answer doctrine by doctrine, party yell by party yell. All this leads to a rapidly escalating hate of the ethnic or nationalistic type than which there is no more stultifying emotion. The hoary instinctual pattern of chin-protruding, hackle-raising collective aggression takes the helm, the hypothalamic regions of the brain rule supreme, enslave the cortex and reduce it to the contemptible task of inventing pseudo-rational justification for unjustifiably irrational behavior. Therewith reason, the only factor able to shun extremes, is removed and the self-exciting swing of the pendulum proceeds undampened, unchecked.

XI. ANTIAUTHORITARIANISM AND AUTHORITARIANISM

It takes some courage to profess that I honestly believe western culture to be on the brink of succumbing to an escalating oscillation of public opinion, swinging between the extremes of an exaggerated antiauthoritarianism and its hateful opposite.

Having witnessed the consequences of authoritarian fascism and still witnessing the tyranny of allegedly democratic communist rulers, the public opinion of western democracy reacts by unreasoningly doing the opposite of what these tyrants as well as our own patriarchal and authoritarian forbears have regarded as correct. By this rebound reaction, western civilization is being pushed into extreme attitudes which are so obviously nonsensical that a counterswing of public opinion seems inevitable. Three examples suffice to illustrate my point.

1. In imperialistic Victorian England, in fascist Germany

and in other totalitarian, though allegedly communist, countries, the rulers were and are blithely arrogating the divine
right to decide, all on their own authority, into what sort of
creature the growing child should be moulded and what
means should be employed to literally lick it into shape.
Bodily punishment is still regarded as quite desirable in
some English schools, and Lenin spoke of "social engineering" by means of Pavlovian conditioning as of a perfectly
legitimate and permissible procedure.

As a result of an entirely justified antagonism against these
crude infractions of the human right to freedom, many
parents in our western culture find it quite impossible to
exert any authority at all, thereby causing the most serious
neurotic damage to their offspring. The two sons of a niece
of mine habitually beat and kick her, viciously and dexter-
ously hitting her shins with the sharp edge of their shoe
soles whenever she fails to obey instantaneously their com-
mands. She then makes believe not to notice. This type of
"reacting by not reacting" can be observed in many analogous situations accruing between parents and their children, as well as between some kindly teachers and their
pupils, and generally between old people and young. The
unexpected and unmotivated attack from the side of a loved
one evidently elicits a feeling of *guilt*, which explains why
the unjustly punished adults even seem to get some sort of
masochistic kick out of getting kicked.

2. In all the above-mentioned authoritarian cultures,
schooling schedules have been strictly laid down, the
suitability of a youngster for a certain type of education
decided by psychological test and no freedom of choice left
to the individual. The incredible idea of organizing a school
in which the children themselves decide what to learn can
only be understood, if not quite forgiven, as an effect of
the rebound from authoritarian schooling programs.

An established position in the rank-order of a social
group is as indispensable to the mental health of a child,

as is the intimate and loving communication with its elders. Because modern children lack both, because they are treated in an excessively antiauthoritarian manner, neurotic symptoms abound in children and adolescents of our time. Curiously enough the high incidence of neurosis often is attributed, by public opinion, to the very opposite of its real cause, i.e. to an excess of paternal authority. A headline in a recent Munich paper read: youth strangles sister out of fear of his parents. In fact, the 17 year old boy had raped his 11 year old sister, she threatened to tell the parents and he killed her to prevent her from doing so. The inference to be drawn was that if the poor boy had not been brought up too authoritatively, he would only have raped the girl, and what a happy family life that would have been.

3. The supreme value which fascist ideology attributes to *health*, to the viability of the individual as well as that of the "race," made it completely blind to the fact that even on the basis of purely biological considerations there is, besides the scale of values between illness and health, an equally important but altogether different one, that which ranges from the lower to the higher organisms. These are independent parameters, the higher organism or the higher culture is by no means better adapted and more likely to survive than is the lower one. Exclusive valuation of health led to the deeply inhuman concept of "lebens-unwertes Leben"—life not worth to be continued—which, like other pseudo-Darwinistic slogans, served as a justification to kill thousands of inmates of mental institutions and millions of people of "inferior" races. On a cultural level, the concept of "entartete Kunst"—degenerated art—led to analogous if less bloody vandalism. The horror which these atrocities have left in all our minds and the consequent rebound of public opinion in the opposite direction have some curious and dangerous consequences. The fact that people *are* genetically different from each other and that a neurotic mass murderer *is* indeed of lesser value to human society than a

normal and responsible member, is strictly taboo and nobody ever dares to confess his belief that it is so. In a lecture on juvenile delinquency, delivered at the Menninger Clinic in 1960, Prof. Frederic Hacker reported a case history of an adolescent who, with malice aforethought, had killed a man, was interned in a clinic as a neurotic, released as completely cured after an alarmingly short period, killed another man within months, and was allowed to run through this sequence of events not less than four times!

I do not pretend to know what should humanely be done with neurotic murderers; an affluent country might keep them in a highly guilded cage. I do know, however, what should *not* be done to them: they should not be told that their misdeed is not really their own fault, but that of an unlucky environment into which they happened to have been born. This is one of the lies of pseudo-democratic doctrine which does very great damage by not only relieving the subject of his responsibility but actually depriving him of it, which means depriving him of one of the most specifically human prerogatives of Mankind.

Though I do not think that I have in any way exaggerated the danger of our present situation, I do not regard it as hopeless by any means. The behavior which our western culture is showing collectively closely resembles that displayed by a neurotic individual. I believe that it is quite correct to speak of a mass neurosis. In principle, the vicious cycle of a neurosis can be interrupted by making its causes conscious to the patient. The causes which effect the present dangerous oscillation of opinion are quite easily accessible to the insight of any average person, and adequate mass education could go far in re-establishing reason to its indispensable function.

Bibliography

Altmann, M. "Patterns of Social Behaviour in Big Game of the United States and Europe." Trans. North Amer. Wildlife Conf. 21 (1956) 538-545.

Berger, Peter L. and Thomas Luckmann. "The Social Construction of Reality." Doubleday, Inc., New York (1966).

Campbell, D. T. "Evolutionary Epistemology" in Schilpp, P. A. "The Philosophy of Karl R. Popper." La Salle: Open Court Publishing Co. (1966).

Erikson, E. H. "Ontogeny of Ritualisation in Man." Philosophical Transactions, Royal Society, London 251 B (1966), 337-349.

Gehlen, A. "Der Mensch, seine Natur und seine Stellung in der Welt." Junker und Dürrhaupt, Berlin (1940).

Huxley, J. S. "The Courtship-Habits of the Great Crested Grebe (Podiceps cristatus); with an Addition to the Theory of Sexual Selection. Proc. Zool. Soc. London, 35 (1914), 491-562.

Koenig, Otto. "Kultur und Verhaltensforschung. Einführung in die Kulturethologie." DTV 614, München, (1970).

Lorenz, K. Z. "On Aggression." Harcourt, Brace & World, New York, (1966).

———. "Innate Bases of Learning" in K. H. Pribram "On the Biology of Learning." Harcourt, Brace & World, New York, (1969).

———. "The Enmity between Generations and Its Probable Ethological Causes." Studium Generale 23, 10, (1970), 963-997.

Mayr, E. "Animal Species and Evolution," Cambridge, Harvard Univ. Press (1963).

Mitscherlich, A. "Auf dem Weg zur Vaterlosen Gesellschaft." Piper, München, (1963).

Popper, K. R. "The Logic of Scientific Discovery." New York, Harper & Row (1962).

Pribram, K. H. "The Four R's of Remembering" in "On the Biology of Learning." Harcourt, Brace & World, New York, (1969).

Schramm, G. "Experimentell erzeugtes Leben" in Naturwissenschaft und Medizin, 29 (1969).

Weiss, P. A. "Life, Order and Understanding: A Theme in Three Variations." Special Supplement to Volume VIII of The Graduate Journal, The University of Texas, 157 pp., (1970).

———. "Depolarisation: Pointers to Conceptual Disarmament." Studium Generale, Springer Verlag, 23, 925-940, (1970).

List of Contributors

HELMUT K. BUECHNER, Ph.D.
Senior Ecologist, Office of Environmental Sciences,
Smithsonian Institution, Washington, D.C.
Ph.D. (Oklahoma State University, 1949); Instructor to Professor of Zoology, Washington State University, 1948-1965; Fulbright Research Scholar, Uganda, 1956-1958; Head, Office of Ecology, Smithsonian Institution, 1965-1969.

JAMES S. COLEMAN, Ph.D.
Professor, Department of Social Relations, Johns Hopkins University,
Baltimore, Md.
Ph.D. (Columbia University, 1955); Fellow, Center for Advanced Study in the Behavioral Sciences, 1955-1956; Assistant Professor, University of Chicago, 1956-1959.

JAY W. FORRESTER, S.M., D.E. (hon.), Sc.D. (hon.)
Professor of Management, Alfred P. Sloan School of Management,
Massachusetts Institute of Technology, Cambridge, Mass.
S.M. (Massachusetts Institute of Technology, 1945); Director, M.I.T. Computer Laboratory, and Head, Digital Computer Division, Lincoln Laboratory till 1956.

KONRAD LORENZ, Dr. med., Dr. phil., Ph.D. (hon.), Dr. med. (hon.), Sc.D. (hon.)
Director, Research Department, Max-Planck-Institute for Physiology
of Behavior, Seewiesen, Germany.
Dr. Med (University of Vienna, 1928); Dr. phil. (University of Vienna, 1933); Lect. comparative anatomy, psychology, University Vienna, 1937-1940; Professor, Psychology, University Königsberg, 1940-1942; Inst. Comp. Ethol., Altenberg, 1949-1951; Director at Max-Planck-Institute for Physiology of Behavior since 1951.

DAVID McNEILL, Ph.D.
Professor of Psychology, University of Chicago, Chicago, Ill.
Ph.D. (University of California, Berkeley, 1962); Associate and Assistant Professor, University of Michigan, 1965-1968; Visiting Associate Professor, Harvard University, 1968-1969.

HASAN OZBEKHAN, M.S.C.
Professor and Member Management Science Center, Wharton School
of Finance and Commerce (University of Pennsylvania), Philadelphia,
Pa.
M.S.C. (University of London, 1945); U.S. Brenner Corp. (N.Y.), 1946-1954; Sr. Consultant, General Electric Co., Management Research Service, 1955-1963; Professor, School of Business Administr., New York University, 1957-1963; Director of Planning, System Development Corporation, 1963-1969; President, Worldwide Information Systems, Inc., 1969-1971.

PAUL A. WEISS, Ph.D., M.D. (hon.), Sc.D. (hon.) Dr. Med. & Surg. (hon.)
Professor Emeritus, The Rockefeller University, New York, N.Y.
Ph.D. (University of Vienna, 1922); Assistant Director, Biological Research Institute, Academy of Sciences, Vienna, 1923-1929; Rockefeller Fellow, 1927-1929; Sterling Fellow, Yale University, 1931-1933; Professor of Zoology, University of Chicago, 1933-1954; Member and Professor, The Rockefeller University since 1954.